100 MENTAL MATHS

100 MENTAL MATHS ACTIVITIES

YEAR 4

Margaret Gronow, Lesley Fletcher and Joan Nield

Authors
Margaret Gronow
Lesley Fletcher
Joan Nield

Illustrations
Louise Gardner

Series Designer
Sonja Bagley

Designer
Quadrum Solutions Ltd.

Mixed Sources
Product group from well-managed forests and other controlled sources
www.fsc.org Cert no. TT-COC-002769
© 1996 Forest Stewardship Council
FSC

Designed using Adobe InDesign

Published by Scholastic Ltd
Book End
Range Road
Witney
Oxfordshire OX29 0YD

www.scholastic.co.uk

Printed by Bell and Bain Ltd, Glasgow

1 2 3 4 5 6 7 8 9 0 1 2 3 4 5 6 7 8 9

British Library Cataloguing-in-Publication Data
A catalogue record for this book is available from the British Library.

ISBN 978-1407-11418-7

CONTENTS

Introduction

About the series

100 Mental Maths Activities is a series of six photocopiable teachers' resource books, one for each of Years 1-6. Each book offers a bank of mental maths activities, each designed to last between five and ten minutes. The activities are designed to fit the planning guidelines of the *Renewed Framework for Teaching Mathematics* (2007) and are therefore divided into five Blocks with three Units of work in each Block.

This series provides a valuable accompaniment to *100 Maths Framework Lessons* (Scholastic, 2007). The mental maths activities are designed to accompany lessons in the Framework series and grids are provided at the start of each Block to indicate the lesson and page numbers of the associated lesson plans in the relevant *100 Maths Framework Lessons* book. Used together, the teacher will have a rich bank of resources, activities and questions, offering greater choice and variety, while keeping to a closely similar mathematical content and progression. It is for the teacher to decide when to repeat an activity and when to move on: the exact mix of consolidation and progression needed will vary from one class to another. However, the series is also wholly appropriate for independent use alongside any maths scheme of work.

The six Rs of oral and mental work

In addition to matching the content of the Renewed Framework, this series also reflects the six features of children's mathematical learning that oral and mental work can support identified by the Primary National Strategy when renewing the Framework. The 'six Rs' provide a valuable guide to the purposes of each starter and a 'type of starter' is offered alongside each of the activities in this book.

The six types of starter include:

- rehearse: practising and consolidating known skills
- recall: securing knowledge of facts – usually number facts
- refresh: drawing on, revisiting or assessing previous knowledge and skills
- refine: sharpening methods and procedures (eg mental strategies)
- read: using mathematical vocabulary and interpreting mathematical images, diagrams and vocabulary correctly
- reason: using and applying acquired knowledge and skills; using reasoning to draw conclusions.

For further information on the 'six Rs' visit the National Strategies website: *www.nationalstrategies.standards.dcsf.gov.uk*.

About the book

Each book provides support for teachers through 15 units of mental maths, developing and practising skills that will have been introduced, explained and explored in your main maths lesson time. Few resources are needed, and the questions for each activity are provided in full. The books are complete with answers, ready for you to pick up and use.

The activities are suitable for use with single- or mixed-ability groups and single- or mixed-age classes, as much emphasis has been placed on the use of differentiated and open-ended questions. Differentiated questions ensure that all the children can be included in each lesson and have the chance to succeed; suitable questions can be directed at chosen individuals, almost guaranteeing success and thus increased confidence.

Several essential photocopiable resource pages are also included (see pages 87–95). These resources are listed alongside each activity where required and should be prepared in advance of each mental maths session.

Each activity in this book has one or more learning objective based on the Year 4 teaching programme in the Renewed Framework. Curriculum grids are presented at the start of each Block to assist teachers with their planning and to highlight links with the related *100 Maths Framework Lessons* title. Alongside the activity description, required resources are highlighted, as well as the 'type of starter' (see above for further information). Where appropriate a 'mental strategy' for solving a number sentence or problem is suggested. Discussion of the children's methods is encouraged, since this will help the children to develop mathematical language skills: to appreciate that no single method is necessarily 'correct' and that a flexible repertoire of approaches is useful; to improve their overall confidence as they come to realise that all responses have value. Strategies are encouraged that will enable the children to progress from the known to the unknown number facts, thus developing their ability to select and use methods of mental calculation.

In Year 4, emphasis is placed on strategies for addition and subtraction (especially with a total of 100), including adding from the larger number, counting up for a small difference, partitioning, and using doubles or near doubles. There are repeated opportunities to reinforce understanding of place value. The relationships between different times tables are used to support the learning of new tables. Games are included in each term's work to help provide variety and generate enthusiasm for numbers. Open-ended questions are used to challenge the children and extend their thinking.

By following the lessons in this series of books, children will develop a variety of strategies for the solution of mathematical problems and will learn to be flexible in their approach to numerical work.

Transitional assessments

Transition is a time when, historically, children dip in their performance. Why this occurs is open to discussion but schools are increasingly aware of the need to accurately track children during these periods in order to ensure, as far as possible, a smooth learning journey. Transitional assessment is therefore important not just as a tool for summative judgements at the end of a school year, but also for communicating with teaching colleagues across the school.

100 Mental Maths Activities Year 4 includes three photocopiable single-level transitional assessments for levels 3 and 4, which will provide evidence of where children have reached in relation to national standards. Printable tests, mark schemes and answer sheets are available on pages 96-111.

BLOCK A

Unit 1

100 Mental Maths Starters				100 Maths Lessons		
Page	Objective	Activity title	Starter type	Unit	Lesson	Page
8	Partition, round and order four-digit whole numbers; use positive and negative numbers in context and position them on a number line; state inequalities using the symbols < and > (e.g. −3 > −5, −1 < +1)	(1) Place value practice	Refresh	1	2	10
8	Partition, round and order four-digit whole numbers; use positive and negative numbers in context and position them on a number line; state inequalities using the symbols < and > (e.g. −3 > −5, −1 < +1)	(2) Which digit?	Refresh	1	2 or 3	10 or 11
9	Use knowledge of addition and subtraction facts and place value to derive sums and differences of pairs of multiples of 10, 100 or 1000	(3) Addition facts to 20	Recall	1	4	12
10	Add or subtract mentally pairs of two-digit whole numbers (e.g. 47 + 58, 91 − 35)	(4) In the family	Recall	1	5	12
10	Derive and recall multiplication facts up to 10 × 10, the corresponding division facts and multiples of numbers to 10 up to the tenth multiple	(5) Tables bingo (2, 5, 10)	Recall	1	6	14
11	Identify the doubles of two-digit numbers; use these to calculate doubles of multiples of 10 and 100 and derive the corresponding halves	(6) Double time	Refine	1	8	15

Unit 2

100 Mental Maths Starters				100 Maths Lessons		
Page	Objective	Activity title	Starter type	Unit	Lesson	Page
11	Use decimal notation for tenths and hundredths and partition decimals; relate the notation to money and measurement; position one-place and two-place decimals on a number line	(7) Parts of a metre	Rehearse	2	1	21
12	Use decimal notation for tenths and hundredths and partition decimals; relate the notation to money and measurement; position one-place and two-place decimals on a number line	(8) Decimal number lines	Rehearse	2	2	22

SCHOLASTIC

Unit 2 ...continued

100 Mental Maths Starters				100 Maths Lessons		
Page	**Objective**	**Activity title**	**Starter type**	**Unit**	**Lesson**	**Page**
12	Report solutions to puzzles and problems, giving explanations and reasoning orally and in writing, using diagrams and symbols	9 Which number?	Reason	2	3	23
13	Add or subtract mentally pairs of two-digit whole numbers (e.g. 47 + 58, 91 − 35)	10 Number splits	Refine	2	4	24
13	Multiply and divide numbers to 1000 by 10 and then 100 (whole-number answers), understanding the effect; relate to scaling up or down	11 Times 10	Refresh	2	7	27
14	Multiply and divide numbers to 1000 by 10 and then 100 (whole-number answers), understanding the effect; relate to scaling up or down	12 Divide by 10	Refresh	2	8	28

Unit 3

100 Mental Maths Starters				100 Maths Lessons		
Page	**Objective**	**Activity title**	**Starter type**	**Unit**	**Lesson**	**Page**
14	Solve one-step and two-step problems involving numbers, money or measures, including time; choose and carry out appropriate calculations, using calculator methods where appropriate	13 Operation!	Reason	3	3	36
15	Use knowledge of rounding, number operations and inverses to estimate and check calculations	14 Quick check	Read	3	4	36
15	Add or subtract mentally pairs of two-digit whole numbers (e.g. 47 + 58, 91 − 35)	15 Missing number	Rehearse	3	7	39
16	Partition, round and order four-digit whole numbers; use positive and negative numbers in context and position them on a number line; state inequalities using the symbols < and > (e.g. −3 > −5, −1 < +1)	16 Put up the number	Rehearse	3	8	39
16	Use decimal notation for tenths and hundredths and partition decimals; relate the notation to money and measurement; position one-place and two-place decimals on a number line	17 How much?	Rehearse	3	10	40

1 Place value practice

Resources
Four sets of 0–9 numeral cards (from photocopiable page 89)

Learning objective
Partition, round and order four-digit whole numbers; use positive and negative numbers in context and position them on a number line; state inequalities using the symbols $<$ and $>$ (e.g. $-3 > -5$, $-1 < +1$)

Type of starter
Refresh

No set answers

Divide the class into four groups: 'thousands', 'hundreds', 'tens' and 'units'. Give each child one number card (the 0 card will not be needed for the 'thousands' group).

Say a three-digit number, for example: *245.* The children holding the correct cards stand together to show the number, which the whole class says.

1. 16
2. 74
3. 45
4. 261
5. 829
6. 193
7. 587
8. 750
9. 3512
10. 6438
11. 4093
12. 8126
13. 1507

2 Which digit?

Resources
Paper

Learning objective
Partition, round and order four-digit whole numbers; use positive and negative numbers in context and position them on a number line; state inequalities using the symbols $<$ and $>$ (e.g. $-3 > -5$, $-1 < +1$)

Type of starter
Refresh

Mental strategy
Knowing which digit represents the tens, hundreds or thousands
Knowing that if a digit is 5 or more it must be rounded up

Answers

1. 4500
2. 8700
3. 9400
4. 6000
5. 4000
6. 73,000
7. 3180
8. 8640
9. 45,680

Write each number (see below) in turn on the board.

For questions 1–3, ask the children to round the numbers to the nearest hundred.

For questions 4–6, ask them to round the numbers to the nearest thousand.

For questions 7–9, ask them to round the numbers to the nearest ten.

After marking each section, ask: *Which digit did you need to round up/down? How did you know that it was that digit?*

1. 4532
2. 8652
3. 9378
4. 5687
5. 4382
6. 72,653
7. 3175
8. 8643
9. 45,676

3 Addition facts to 20

Learning objective Use knowledge of addition and subtraction facts and place value to derive sums and differences of pairs of multiples of 10, 100 or 1000 **Type of starter** Recall	**Resources** None

Ask quick-fire questions. Children raise a hand to answer.

1. Add 6 and 5 together.
2. 4 + 12
3. 2 + 7
4. Double 9
5. 13 + 5
6. 11 + 4
7. 8 + 9
8. 4 + 5
9. What is the total of 3 and 8?
10. Double 12
11. 15 + 3
12. 10 plus 7
13. Double 19
14. What is 6 more than 9?
15. 5 + 7

Answers

1. 11
2. 16
3. 9
4. 18
5. 18
6. 15
7. 17
8. 9
9. 11
10. 24
11. 18
12. 17
13. 38
14. 15
15. 12

4 In the family

Resources	Learning objective
None	Add or subtract mentally pairs of two-digit whole numbers (e.g. 47 + 58, 91 − 35)
	Type of starter Recall

Answers

1-6. 16 − 9 = 7 (or 16 − 7 = 9) and so on

7-12. 3 + 9 = 12 (or 9 + 3 = 12) and so on

Read out each addition fact or write them on the board. The children say a subtraction fact based on it.

Repeat for the subtraction facts (children say an addition fact).

1. 7 + 9 = 16	5. 14 + 9 = 23	9. 24 − 13 = 11
2. 12 + 8 = 20	6. 23 + 12 = 35	10. 57 − 36 = 21
3. 6 + 11 = 17	7. 12 − 3 = 9	11. 63 − 24 = 39
4. 15 + 16 = 31	8. 15 − 8 = 7	12. 38 − 27 = 11

5 Tables bingo (2, 5, 10)

Resources	Learning objective
Paper and a pencil for each child	Derive and recall multiplication facts up to 10 × 10, the corresponding division facts and multiples of numbers to 10 up to the tenth multiple
	Type of starter Recall

Answers

1. 6	9. 25
2. 40	10. 90
3. 10	11. 30
4. 100	12. 4
5. 45	13. 5
6. 70	14. 12
7. 35	15. 18
8. 80	16. 2

Ask the children to choose five numbers from the 2-, 5- and 10-times tables and write them spread out on their paper.

Read out the questions (use: *times, multiplied by, double* and *what is the product of ...?*). If the children have the answer to a question on their paper, they cross it out. The first child to cross out all five numbers wins.

1. 3 × 2	5. 9 × 5	9. 5 × 5	13. 1 × 5
2. 4 × 10	6. 7 × 10	10. 9 × 10	14. 6 × 2
3. 2 × 5	7. 7 × 5	11. 6 × 5	15. 2 × 9
4. 10 × 10	8. 8 × 10	12. 2 × 2	16. 1 × 2

6 Double time

Learning objective
Identify the doubles of two-digit numbers; use these to calculate doubles of multiples of 10 and 100 and derive the corresponding halves

Type of starter
Refine

Resources
Board or flipchart

Write *double 27* = on the board. Remind the children to use partitioning, or near doubles with adjustment. For example:

2 × 27 = (2 × 20) + (2 × 7) = 40 + 14 = 54

or 2 × 27 = (2 × 25) + (2 × 2) = 50 + 4 = 54

Ask the children to double the following numbers (use: *Double ..., 2 times ...* and *Add ... to itself*).

1. 9	5. 42	9. 31	13. 35
2. 14	6. 16	10. 37	14. 50
3. 25	7. 28	11. 12	15. 44
4. 33	8. 48	12. 19	16. 16

Answers

1. 18	9. 62
2. 28	10. 74
3. 50	11. 24
4. 66	12. 38
5. 84	13. 70
6. 32	14. 100
7. 56	15. 88
8. 96	16. 32

7 Parts of a metre

Unit 2

Learning objective
Use decimal notation for tenths and hundredths and partition decimals; relate the notation to money and measurement; position one-place and two-place decimals on a number line

Type of starter
Rehearse

Mental strategy
Knowing 100 centimetres = 1.0 metre
Knowing 10 centimetres = 0.1 metre

Resources
Metre ruler

Show children the metre ruler.

As you ask questions 1–10, point to the appropriate place on the ruler.

Record these lengths in metres:

1. 100cm	2. 10cm	3. 30cm	4. 25cm

Record these lengths in centimetres:

5. 0.2m	6. 0.8m	7. 0.75m	8. 1.2m

Which is longer:

9. 10cm or 0.2m?	11. 50cm or 0.25m?
10. 0.4m or 30cm?	12. 0.75m or 80cm?

Answers

1. 1.0m	7. 75cm
2. 0.1m	8. 120cm
3. 0.3m	9. 0.2m
4. 0.25m	10. 0.4m
5. 20cm	11. 50cm
6. 80cm	12. 80cm

8 Decimal number lines

Resources
Decimal number lines for each child (from photocopiable page 91); on the board: decimal number line to match lines on photocopiable page 91

Learning objective
Use decimal notation for tenths and hundredths and partition decimals; relate the notation to money and measurement; position one-place and two-place decimals on a number line

Type of starter
Rehearse

Mental strategy
Understanding of place value and decimal notation

Answers

Check marks on number lines; answers should show:

1. 2.72 > 2.27
2. 2.61 > 2.16
3. 2.83 > 2.38
4. 2.94 > 2.49

Write each pair of numbers (see below) in turn on the board. Ask the children to estimate and mark the position of each pair on the number line (they should use a different line for each pair).

Then ask different children to mark each number on the number line on the board. For each pair of numbers ask: *Which was the bigger/smaller number? How do you know? Which digits helped you, when positioning the numbers?*

1. 2.72 and 2.27
2. 2.61 and 2.16
3. 2.83 and 2.38
4. 2.94 and 2.49

9 Which number?

Resources
A pencil and paper for each child may be useful

Learning objective
Report solutions to puzzles and problems, giving explanations and reasoning orally and in writing, using diagrams and symbols

Type of starter
Reason

Answers

1. 8
2. 9
3. 21
4. 5
5. 20

Work through the first question together, listing possible outcomes that satisfy the first rule, then choosing the answer that also satisfies the second rule.

Ask: *What number am I?*

1. I am an even number between 5 and 10. I am a multiple of 4.
2. I am an odd number between 4 and 10. I am a multiple of 3.
3. I am an odd number between 20 and 26. I am a multiple of 3.
4. If I double this number, the answer is half of 20.
5. I am an even number between 16 and 26. I am a multiple of 5.

10 Number splits

Learning objective
Add or subtract mentally pairs of two-digit whole numbers (e.g. 47 + 58, 91 – 35)

Type of starter
Refine

Resources
Board or flipchart

Write *46 + 27* = on the board.

Ask for the answer and strategies to solve it. Stress the advantages of partitioning: 40 + 20 then 6 + 7 → 60 + 13 = 73 or 46 + 20 then 66 + 7 = 73.

Ask these questions, occasionally asking a child to explain a method used.

1. 26 + 35	5. 27 + 35	9. 52 + 29
2. 28 + 34	6. 16 + 38	10. 37 + 47
3. 23 + 48	7. 34 + 29	11. 36 + 57
4. 19 + 26	8. 25 + 58	12. 28 + 49

Answers

1. 61	7. 63
2. 62	8. 83
3. 71	9. 81
4. 45	10. 84
5. 62	11. 93
6. 54	12. 77

11 Times 10

Learning objective
Multiply and divide numbers to 1000 by 10 and then 100 (whole-number answers), understanding the effect; relate to scaling up or down

Type of starter
Refresh

Resources
Board or flipchart

Write *15 × 10 = 150* on the board. Remind the class that when we multiply by 10, the digits move one place to the left. The zero is added as a 'place holder' to keep them there.

Ask the children to multiply the following numbers by 10 (use: *times, multiply ... by 10, make ... 10 times bigger*).

1. 5	6. 11	11. 58	16. 28
2. 8	7. 24	12. 16	17. 56
3. 2	8. 39	13. 41	18. 65
4. 13	9. 46	14. 34	19. 40
5. 17	10. 72	15. 50	20. 69

Answers

1. 50	11. 580
2. 80	12. 160
3. 20	13. 410
4. 130	14. 340
5. 170	15. 500
6. 110	16. 280
7. 240	17. 560
8. 390	18. 650
9. 460	19. 400
10. 720	20. 690

12 Divide by 10

Resources
Board or flipchart

Learning objective
Multiply and divide numbers to 1000 by 10 and then 100 (whole-number answers), understanding the effect; relate to scaling up or down

Type of starter
Refresh

Answers

1.	4	11.	6
2.	9	12.	18
3.	3	13.	24
4.	12	14.	57
5.	16	15.	11
6.	28	16.	82
7.	45	17.	90
8.	50	18.	69
9.	37	19.	52
10.	71	20.	76

Write 70 ÷ 10 = 7 on the board. Remind the class that when we divide by 10, the digits move one place to the right.

Ask the children to divide the following numbers by 10 (use: *divided by, make ... 10 times smaller and what is one tenth of ... ?*).

1.	40	6.	280	11.	60	16.	820
2.	90	7.	450	12.	180	17.	900
3.	30	8.	500	13.	240	18.	690
4.	120	9.	370	14.	570	19.	520
5.	160	10.	710	15.	110	20.	760

Unit 3

13 Operation!

Resources
Individual whiteboard for each child; on the board: large mathematical signs: +, −, × and ÷

Learning objective
Solve one-step and two-step problems involving numbers, money or measures, including time; choose and carry out appropriate calculations, using calculator methods where appropriate

Type of starter
Reason

Mental strategy
Choosing the appropriate operation

Answers
1. × (£8.75)
2. ÷ (8 buses)
3. + (300)
4. − and ÷ (32p)
5. × (5.2)

Show the children the signs on the board. Explain that they must decide which operation(s) to use for each of the following problems and write them on their boards.

1. Tickets for the football match cost £1.75 each. How much will five cost?
2. There are 224 children in our school. How many buses will I need to book for our school trip, if each one holds 30 people?
3. What is the sum of 60 and 240?
4. I had £2. I bought three packets of crisps and got £1.04 change. How much did each packet cost?
5. What is double 2.6?

14 Quick check

Learning objective
Use knowledge of rounding, number operations and inverses to estimate and check calculations

Type of starter
Read

Resources
Board or flipchart

Write *8 + 6 = 14* on the board. Ask how subtraction could be used to check the answer (14 – 6 = 8 or 14 – 8 = 6).

Read the addition statements or write them on the board. Children raise a hand to give a subtraction 'check' for each statement.

Repeat for the subtraction statements (children give an addition 'check').

1. 6 + 4 = 10
2. 8 + 7 = 15
3. 11 + 9 = 20
4. 13 + 12 = 25
5. 7 + 2 = 9
6. 3 + 14 = 17
7. 12 – 8 = 4
8. 6 – 1 = 5
9. 17 – 15 = 2
10. 9 – 5 = 4
11. 19 – 6 = 13
12. 21 – 12 = 9

Answers

1-6. 10 – 4 = 6 (or 10 – 6 = 4) and so on

7-12. 8 + 4 = 12 (or 4 + 8 = 12) and so on

15 Missing number

Learning objective
Add or subtract mentally pairs of two-digit whole numbers (e.g. 47 + 58, 91 – 35)

Type of starter
Rehearse

Resources
None

Read each statement, then pause. The children together say the missing number on a silent signal from you (such as a raised hand).

1. 4 + ? = 10
2. 9 + ? = 12
3. ? + 13 = 26
4. ? + 18 = 35
5. 20 – ? = 13
6. 24 – ? = 15
7. ? – 8 = 2
8. ? – 12 = 13
9. 16 + ? = 31
10. 49 – ? = 22
11. ? – 0 = 29
12. ? + 19 = 60
13. 17 + ? = 25
14. ? – 16 = 4
15. ? + 20 = 41

Answers

1. 6
2. 3
3. 13
4. 17
5. 7
6. 9
7. 10
8. 25
9. 15
10. 27
11. 29
12. 41
13. 8
14. 20
15. 21

16 Put up the number

Resources
Three sets of 0–9 numeral cards (from photocopiable page 89)

Learning objective
Partition, round and order four-digit whole numbers; use positive and negative numbers in context and position them on a number line; state inequalities using the symbols < and > (e.g. −3 > −5, −1 < +1)

Type of starter
Rehearse

No set answers

Divide the class into three groups: 'hundreds', 'tens' and 'units'. Give each child one number card (the 0 card will not be needed for the hundreds group).

Say a two-digit number, for example: *43*. The children holding the correct cards stand together to show the number, which the whole class says.

1.	27	5.	68	9.	902	13.	399
2.	45	6.	241	10.	180	14.	535
3.	70	7.	564	11.	476	15.	658
4.	32	8.	817	12.	723	16.	260

17 How much?

Resources
On the board: large number line (see activity)

Learning objective
Use decimal notation for tenths and hundredths and partition decimals; relate the notation to money and measurement; position one-place and two-place decimals on a number line

Type of starter
Rehearse

Mental strategy
Converting pence in £s and pence using decimal notation

Answers
1. £1.90
2. £2.40
3. £3.65
4. £4.10
5. £0.80
6. 130p
7. 20p
8. 490p
9. 275p
10. 330p

Show the children the number line below. Explain that they will be using it to help them use decimal notation for writing amounts of money.

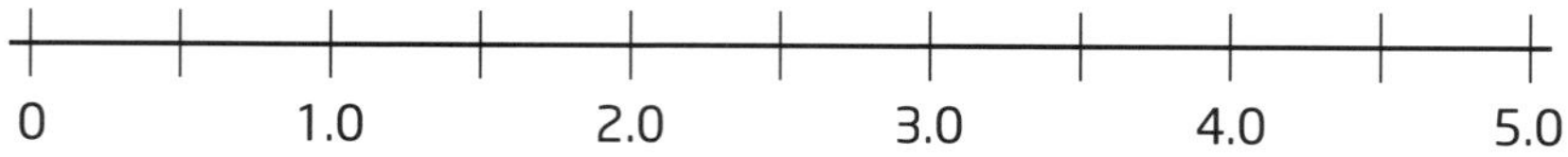

Say: *I will say an amount of money in pence. I want you to write it in pounds and pence, using decimal notation.* Read the amounts in questions 1–5.

Say: *I will now say an amount of money in pounds and pence. This time I want you to write it in pence.* Read the amounts in questions 6–10.

1.	190p	6.	£1.30
2.	240p	7.	£0.20
3.	365p	8.	£4.90
4.	410p	9.	£2.75
5.	80p	10.	£3.30

BLOCK B

Unit 1

100 Mental Maths Starters				100 Maths Lessons		
Page	**Objective**	**Activity title**	**Starter type**	**Unit**	**Lesson**	**Page**
19	Use knowledge of rounding, number operations and inverses to estimate and check calculations	18 Up or down?	Rehearse	1	1	48
19	Derive and recall multiplication facts up to 10 × 10, the corresponding division facts and multiples of numbers to 10 up to the tenth multiple	19 Know your times tables	Recall	1	2	48
20	Identify and use patterns, relationships and properties of numbers or shapes; investigate a statement involving numbers and test it with examples	20 Clap counter	Rehearse	1	4	50
20	Use knowledge of addition and subtraction facts and place value to derive sums and differences of pairs of multiples of 10, 100 or 1000	21 Make 100	Recall	1	6	51
21	Solve one-step and two-step problems involving numbers, money or measures, including time; choose and carry out appropriate calculations, using calculator methods where appropriate	22 What's missing?	Reason	1	9	53
22	Visualise 3D objects from 2D drawings; make nets of common solids	23 What's my shape?	Read	1	10	53
23	Draw polygons and classify them by identifying their properties, including their line symmetry	24 Symmetry and polygons	Recall	1	12 or 13	55 or 56
24	Report solutions to puzzles and problems, giving explanations and reasoning orally and in writing, using diagrams and symbols	25 Sorting 2D shapes	Reason/read	1	14 or 15	57

Unit 2

100 Mental Maths Starters				100 Maths Lessons		
Page	**Objective**	**Activity title**	**Starter type**	**Unit**	**Lesson**	**Page**
25	Identify and use patterns, relationships and properties of numbers or shapes; investigate a statement involving numbers and test it with examples	26 Odd and even (1)	Reason	2	4	65
25	Report solutions to puzzles and problems, giving explanations and reasoning orally and in writing, using diagrams and symbols	27 Odd and even (2)	Reason	2	5	66

Unit 2 ...continued

100 Mental Maths Starters				100 Maths Lessons		
Page	Objective	Activity title	Starter type	Unit	Lesson	Page
26	Use knowledge of rounding, number operations and inverses to estimate and check calculations	28 Inverse operations	Recall	2	7	68
26	Identify the doubles of two-digit numbers; use these to calculate doubles of multiples of 10 and 100 and derive the corresponding halves	29 Double number chains (1)	Recall	2	8	69
27	Derive and recall multiplication facts up to 10 × 10, the corresponding division facts and multiples of numbers to 10 up to the tenth multiple	30 Tables snap	Recall	2	9	69
27	Derive and recall multiplication facts up to 10 × 10, the corresponding division facts and multiples of numbers to 10 up to the tenth multiple	31 8 times	Recall	2	10	70
28	Draw polygons and classify them by identifying their properties, including their line symmetry	32 True or false?	Reason	2	13	73
28	Visualise 3D objects from 2D drawings; make nets of common solids	33 Shape snap	Read	2	15	74

Unit 3

100 Mental Maths Starters				100 Maths Lessons		
Page	Objective	Activity title	Starter type	Unit	Lesson	Page
29	Identify and use patterns, relationships and properties of numbers or shapes; investigate a statement involving numbers and test it with examples	34 Number patterns	Reason	3	3	79
30	Solve one-step and two-step problems involving numbers, money or measures, including time; choose and carry out appropriate calculations, using calculator methods where appropriate	35 Addition and subtraction words	Rehearse	3	4	79
30	Report solutions to puzzles and problems, giving explanations and reasoning orally and in writing, using diagrams and symbols	36 Number sequences	Reason	3	5	80
31	Use knowledge of rounding, number operations and inverses to estimate and check calculations	37 Estimating and checking	Refine	3	8	82
32	Use knowledge of addition and subtraction facts and place value to derive sums and differences of pairs of multiples of 10, 100 or 1000	38 Total 100	Rehearse	3	9	84
32	Identify the doubles of two-digit numbers; use these to calculate doubles of multiples of 10 and 100 and derive the corresponding halves	39 Double number chains (2)	Rehearse	3	10	84
33	Derive and recall multiplication facts up to 10 × 10, the corresponding division facts and multiples of numbers to 10 up to the tenth multiple	40 Times tables facts	Recall	3	11	85
33	Visualise 3D objects from 2D drawings; make nets of common solids	41 Describing 3D shapes	Rehearse	3	15	87

18 Up or down?

Learning objective
Use knowledge of rounding, number operations and inverses to estimate and check calculations

Type of starter
Rehearse

Mental strategy
If the last digit is 5, 6, 7, 8 or 9 round up; otherwise round down

Resources
None

Say a number. Ask: *To round to the nearest 10* (questions 1-10), *100* (questions 11-15), *whole number* (questions 16-20), *does it need to go up or down?*

1. 27	6. 161	11. 161	16. 3.4
2. 31	7. 243	12. 243	17. 3.6
3. 75	8. 487	13. 487	18. 4.1
4. 102	9. 611	14. 611	19. 4.5
5. 137	10. 492	15. 492	20. 7.7

Answers

1. Up	11. Up
2. Down	12. Down
3. Up	13. Up
4. Down	14. Down
5. Up	15. Up
6. Down	16. Down
7. Down	17. Up
8. Up	18. Down
9. Down	19. Up
10. Down	20. Up

19 Know your times tables

Learning objective
Derive and recall multiplication facts up to 10 × 10, the corresponding division facts and multiples of numbers to 10 up to the tenth multiple

Type of starter
Recall

Resources
None

Ask quick-fire questions (use: *times, multiplied by, what is the product of ... ?*). Children raise a hand to answer.

1. 4 × 2	6. 4 × 5	11. 6 × 10
2. 10 × 5	7. 5 × 10	12. 7 × 5
3. 3 × 10	8. 10 × 2	13. 1 × 2
4. 2 × 5	9. 7 × 10	14. 4 × 10
5. 2 × 3	10. 2 × 7	15. 8 × 5

Answers

1. 8	9. 70
2. 50	10. 14
3. 30	11. 60
4. 10	12. 35
5. 6	13. 2
6. 20	14. 40
7. 50	15. 40
8. 20	

20 Clap counter

Resources None	**Learning objective** Identify and use patterns, relationships and properties of numbers or shapes; investigate a statement involving numbers and test it with examples **Type of starter** Rehearse

No set answers

Ask the children to count together in tens from the start number (questions 1-8). Each time you clap your hands, they should reverse the direction of the count.

Repeat for counting in hundreds (questions 9-16).

1. 23	5. 26	9. 428	13. 298
2. 57	6. 32	10. 205	14. 149
3. 11	7. 45	11. 512	15. 376
4. 34	8. 69	12. 333	16. 554

21 Make 100

Resources None	**Learning objective** Use knowledge of addition and subtraction facts and place value to derive sums and differences of pairs of multiples of 10, 100 or 1000 **Type of starter** Recall

Answers

1. 20 (4 steps)
2. 40 (8 steps)
3. 25 (5 steps)
4. 55 (11 steps)
5. 85 (17 steps)
6. 50 (10 steps)
7. 65 (13 steps)
8. 80 (16 steps)
9. 40 (8 steps)
10. 70 (14 steps)
11. 15 (3 steps)
12. 30 (6 steps)

Count in fives and then in tens to 100 and back again.

Read out the numbers. Ask the children to raise their hands and say the other one of the pair to total 100. If appropriate, challenge children to say how many steps of 5 they have taken (for example: *I say 80, you say...* '20, four steps of 5').

1. 80	4. 45	7. 35	10. 30
2. 60	5. 15	8. 20	11. 85
3. 75	6. 50	9. 60	12. 70

22 What's missing?

Learning objective
Solve one-step and two-step problems involving numbers, money or measures, including time; choose and carry out appropriate calculations, using calculator methods where appropriate

Type of starter
Reason

Mental strategy
If the answer is a larger number it will either be + or x; if the answer is a smaller number it will be − or ÷

Resources
None

Read out the following questions or write them on the board. Ask children to decide whether the question mark represents a +, −, × or ÷.

1. 17 ? 4 = 21
2. 3 ? 3 = 9
3. 17 ? 7 = 10
4. 24 ? 3 = 8
5. 5 ? 2 = 10
6. 7 ? 3 = 21
7. 18 ? 3 = 6
8. 47 ? 36 = 11
9. 12 ? 17 = 29
10. 80 ? 4 = 320
11. 75 ? 5 = 15
12. 18 ? 4 = 72
13. 25 ? 10 = 250
14. 706 ? 35 = 741
15. 80 ? 10 = 8

Answers
1. +
2. ×
3. −
4. ÷
5. ×
6. ×
7. ÷
8. −
9. +
10. ×
11. ÷
12. ×
13. ×
14. +
15. ÷

23 What's my shape?

Resources
None

Learning objective
Visualise 3D objects from 2D drawings; make nets of common solids

Type of starter
Read

Answers

1. Equilateral triangle
2. Triangular prism
3. Square
4. Regular hexagon
5. Cube
6. Isosceles triangle
7. Square-based pyramid
8. Rectangle or oblong
9. Cylinder
10. Cuboid

Read the following descriptions and ask: *What am I?* after each.

1. I am a 2D shape. I have three sides. All my angles are equal, and my sides are the same length.
2. I am a 3D shape. I will not roll. I have five faces. Two of my faces are triangular and three are rectangular.
3. I am a 2D shape. I am a regular quadrilateral. My sides are of equal length and each of my angles measures 90 degrees.
4. I am a 2D shape. I am a regular polygon. My six sides are of equal length and my six angles are equal.
5. I am a 3D shape. I have twelve edges of equal length, six square faces and eight corners.
6. I am a 2D shape. I am an irregular polygon. Two of my three sides are equal in length and two of my three angles are equal in size.
7. I am a 3D shape. I have five faces. Four of my faces are triangular and my base is square.
8. I am a 2D shape. I am an irregular polygon with four sides. My opposite sides are equal. My four angles are right angles.
9. I am a 3D shape. I can roll. I am made from two circles and a rectangle.
10. I am a 3D irregular polygon. I have six faces. My opposite faces are equal. I have twelve edges and eight corners.

24 Symmetry and polygons

Learning objective
Draw polygons and classify them by identifying their properties, including their line symmetry

Type of starter
Recall

Resources
Pictures of 2D shapes (from photocopiable page 93)

This activity recalls the children's knowledge of the properties of polygons, in particular their lines of symmetry.

Ask the following questions. The children can use the illustrations to help them visualise the lines of symmetry.

1. What is the difference between an equilateral and an isosceles triangle?
2. How many lines of symmetry does an equilateral triangle have?
3. How many lines of symmetry does an isosceles triangle have?
4. What is a scalene triangle?
5. How many lines of symmetry does a scalene triangle have?
6. How many lines of symmetry does a square have?
7. How many lines of symmetry does a rectangle have?
8. How many lines of symmetry does a kite have?
9. A regular pentagon has five equal sides. How many lines of symmetry does it have?
10. A regular hexagon has six equal sides. How many lines of symmetry does it have?

Answers

1. An equilateral triangle has three equal sides and angles but an isosceles triangle has only two equal sides and two equal angles.
2. Three
3. One
4. In a scalene triangle, no sides are equal and no angles are equal.
5. None
6. Four
7. Two
8. One
9. Five
10. Six

25 Sorting 2D shapes

Resources
Carroll diagram and 2D shapes (from photocopiable page 94)

Learning objective
Report solutions to puzzles and problems, giving explanations and reasoning orally and in writing, using diagrams and symbols

Type of starter
Reason/read

Show the children the Carroll diagram. Point out that the criteria are missing.

Ask:

1. What is the criterion for column one?
2. What is the criterion for column two?
3. What is the criterion for row one?
4. What is the criterion for row two?
5. What do all the shapes in column one have in common?
6. What do all the shapes in column two have in common?
7. Explain why shape (a) is not regular.
8. Explain why shape (b) is regular.
9. Name three shapes that are quadrilaterals. Explain why this is true.
10. Explain why a rectangle is not a regular quadrilateral.

Answers
1. Triangles
2. Quadrilaterals
3. Regular
4. Irregular
5. All have three sides and three angles
6. All have four sides and four angles
7. The sides are different lengths and the angles are not equal
8. The sides are equal length and the angles are equal
9. For example: trapezium, kite, rectangle; they all have four sides and four angles
10. The sides are not all equal and the angles are not all equal

26 Odd and even (1)

Learning objective
Identify and use patterns, relationships and properties of numbers or shapes; investigate a statement involving numbers and test it with examples

Type of starter
Reason

Resources
Pencils; odds and evens addition grid (from photocopiable page 88) for each child

Ask: *What do even numbers always end with?* (0, 2, 4, 6 or 8.) *What do odd numbers always end with?* (1, 3, 5, 7 or 9.)

Read out the numbers below. The children together say 'odd' or 'even' after each number.

Give a copy of the odds and evens addition grid to each child to complete after brief discussion. When they have finished, recap: odd + odd = even; even + even = even; odd + even = odd.

1.	16	4.	232	7.	1653	10.	24
2.	128	5.	165	8.	2390		
3.	71	6.	349	9.	5817		

Answers
1. Even
2. Even
3. Odd
4. Even
5. Odd
6. Odd
7. Odd
8. Even
9. Odd
10. Even

27 Odd and even (2)

Learning objective
Report solutions to puzzles and problems, giving explanations and reasoning orally and in writing, using diagrams and symbols

Type of starter
Reason

Resources
On the board: odds and evens addition grid (from photocopiable page 88)

Ask: *Odd + odd = ? Even + even = ? Odd + even = ?* and complete the grid on the board. Ask: *Does the same strategy work for subtraction?* (Yes)

With the children, sort questions 1–12 below into odd/even answers before working out the exact solutions.

If there is time, investigate what happens with multiplication and division.

1.	12 + 17	5.	18 + 6 + 9	9.	18 − 14
2.	13 + 19	6.	13 + 12 + 8	10.	17 − 12
3.	27 + 3	7.	14 + 6 + 7	11.	19 − 3
4.	34 + 2 + 4	8.	16 + 12 + 8	12.	34 − 2 − 4

Answers

Odd
1. 29
5. 33
6. 33
7. 27
10. 5

Even
2. 32
3. 30
4. 40
8. 36
9. 4
11. 16
12. 28

28 Inverse operations

Resources
Paper and a pencil for each pair of children

Learning objective
Use knowledge of rounding, number operations and inverses to estimate and check calculations

Type of starter
Recall

No set answers

Divide the class into mixed-ability pairs. Ask each pair to write an addition statement and a subtraction statement using numbers no bigger than 20. For example:

7 + 5 = 12   18 − 7 = 11

Beneath each one, ask the children to write two statements that use the inverse operation to check the answer. For example:

12 − 5 = 7   7 + 11 = 18

12 − 7 = 5   11 + 7 = 18

Allow two minutes for this. The children then take turns to read a statement and ask the other children for a 'checking' statement.

29 Double number chains (1)

Resources
None

Learning objective
Identify the doubles of two-digit numbers; use these to calculate doubles of multiples of 10 and 100 and derive the corresponding halves

Type of starter
Recall

Answers
1. 10, 20, 40, 80
2. 22, 44, 88
3. 34, 68
4. 12, 24, 48, 96
5. 28, 56
6. 18, 36, 72
7. 46, 92
8. 38, 76
9. 16, 32, 64
10. 42, 84

The children stand in a line or circle. The first child doubles the start number, which is doubled again by the next child, and so on. When a number greater than 100 is needed, that child sits down and is 'out' of the game. The game continues with a new start number.

1. 5
2. 11
3. 17
4. 6
5. 14
6. 9
7. 23
8. 19
9. 8
10. 21

30 Tables snap

Learning objective
Derive and recall multiplication facts up to 10 × 10, the corresponding division facts and multiples of numbers to 10 up to the tenth multiple

Type of starter
Recall

Resources
Tables snap cards (enlarged from photocopiable page 90) – at least one card per child

Deal the cards. Those children who have the answer to a question hold up the card and say 'Snap'.

Finish the activity with rapid answering of all the questions.

1. 8 × 2	5. 7 × 2	9. 5 × 5
2. 6 × 5	6. 9 × 3	10. 9 × 2
3. 9 × 4	7. 8 × 3	11. 7 × 5
4. 8 × 5	8. 6 × 3	12. 4 × 5

Answers
1. 16
2. 30
3. 36
4. 40
5. 14
6. 27
7. 24
8. 18
9. 25
10. 18
11. 35
12. 20

31 8 times

Learning objective
Derive and recall multiplication facts up to 10 × 10, the corresponding division facts and multiples of numbers to 10 up to the tenth multiple

Type of starter
Recall

Resources
A board or flipchart

Write the complete 8-times table as the children say it together. Chant the table forwards and backwards and look at the patterns. Remove the statements already known from other tables.

Ask the children to answer the multiplications in random order, encouraging quick responses from individuals. For example, ask:

1. 5 × 8	5. 2 × 8	9. 6 × 8
2. 3 × 8	6. 9 × 8	10. 8 × 8
3. 7 × 8	7. 4 × 8	
4. 10 × 8	8. 1 × 8	

Answers
1. 40
2. 24
3. 56
4. 80
5. 16
6. 72
7. 32
8. 8
9. 48
10. 64

32 True or false?

Resources
None

Learning objective
Draw polygons and classify them by identifying their properties, including their line symmetry

Type of starter
Reason

Answers
1. True
2. False
3. False
4. True
5. True
6. True
7. True
8. False

Read the following statements and ask: *True or false?*
1. All quadrilaterals have four sides and four angles.
2. All triangles have one right angle.
3. All pentagons have five equal sides and five equal angles.
4. A regular hexagon must have six equal sides and six equal angles.
5. A rhombus is a quadrilateral.
6. An isosceles triangle has two equal sides and two equal angles.
7. An equilateral triangle has three lines of reflective symmetry.
8. A square has a total of two lines of reflective symmetry.

33 Shape snap

Resources
Shape snap cards (enlarged from photocopiable page 87) – at least one card per child

Learning objective
Visualise 3D objects from 2D drawings; make nets of common solids

Type of starter
Read

Answers
1. Equilateral triangle
2. Triangular prism
3. Square
4. Regular hexagon
5. Cube
6. Isosceles triangle
7. Square-based pyramid
8. Rectangle or oblong
9. Cylinder
10. Cuboid

Give each child at least one shape snap card.

Read the shape descriptions from the activity 'What's my shape?' (page 22). The children who have a shape card that matches the description hold their card in the air and say 'Snap'. Ask for the name of the shape.

When all of the shape descriptions have been used, collect the shape cards. Invite a child to take one card from the pile and give clues about the shape. Can the others guess what it is?

34 Number patterns

Learning objective
Identify and use patterns, relationships and properties of numbers or shapes; investigate a statement involving numbers and test it with examples

Type of starter
Reason

Resources
None

Ask the following questions.

1. I know that the answer to 4 × 4 is double the answer to 4 × 2. Explain why this statement is true.
2. I know that 7 × 2 = 14. If I double 14 I get the answer to 7 × 4. If I double this answer, I get the answer to 7 × 8. True or false?
3. 3 × 3 = ? Now use doubling to find the answer to 6 × 6. The answer is 18. True or false? Explain.
4. 4 × 6 and 8 × 3 both have the same answer. How can you explain that this statement is true just by looking at the digits in the question?
5. Complete these number sentences: 4 × 6 = and 8 × 3 =
6. If 7 × 3 = 21, what is 7 × 6?
7. If 12 ÷ 4 = 3, what is 12 ÷ 2?
8. If 16 ÷ 4 = 4, what is 16 ÷ 2?
9. If the divisor is halved what happens to the answer?
10. Give an example of your own like those in questions 7 and 8.

Answers

1. The multiplier is doubled so the answer is doubled.
2. True
3. False. The answer is 36 because both digits have been doubled.
4. In the second question, one of the digits is doubled and the other is halved so the answers will be the same.
5. 24 and 24
6. 42
7. 6
8. 8
9. It is doubled.
10. For example: 18 ÷ 6 = 3 and 18 ÷ 3 = 6

35 Addition and subtraction words

Resources
None

Learning objective
Solve one-step and two-step problems involving numbers, money or measures, including time; choose and carry out appropriate calculations, using calculator methods where appropriate

Type of starter
Rehearse

Answers

1.	7	10.	14
2.	7	11.	9
3.	23	12.	17
4.	17	13.	9
5.	6	14.	21
6.	19	15.	5
7.	7	16.	16
8.	18	17.	11
9.	6	18.	18

Ask the following quick-fire addition and subtraction questions (use: *minus, take, subtract* and *what is the difference between... ?; add, find the total of...* and *find the sum of...*). Allow five seconds between questions.

1.	3 + 4	7.	15 − 8	13.	18 − 9
2.	10 − 3	8.	9 × 2	14.	19 + 2
3.	18 + 5	9.	6 − 0	15.	19 − 14
4.	11 + 6	10.	8 + 6	16.	4 + 7 + 5
5.	13 − 7	11.	14 − 5	17.	11 − 0
6.	15 + 4	12.	6 + 11	18.	9 + 6 + 3

36 Number sequences

Resources
None

Learning objective
Report solutions to puzzles and problems, giving explanations and reasoning orally and in writing, using diagrams and symbols

Type of starter
Reason

Answers

1.	11	13	+2
2.	8	5	−3
3.	32	64	×2
4.	11	16	+1, +2, +3...
5.	2	4	+2
6.	2.5	3.0	+0.5
7.	0.4.	0.6	+0.2
8.	20	15	−5
9.	16	25	+1, +3, +5...
10.	60	45	−15

Ask the children to complete each of these sequences and then explain the pattern or rule.

1. 3, 5, 7, 9, _, _
2. 20, 17, 14, 11, _, _
3. 2, 4, 8, 16, _, _
4. 1, 2, 4, 7, _, _
5. _, _, 6, 8, 10, 12
6. 0.5, 1.0, 1.5, 2.0, _, _
7. 0.2, _, _, 0.8, 1.0, 1.2
8. 30, 25, _, _, 10, 5
9. 0, 1, 4, 9, _, _
10. 90, 75, _, _, 30, 15

37 Estimating and checking

Learning objective
Use knowledge of rounding, number operations and inverses to estimate and check calculations

Type of starter
Refine

Resources
None

Ask the children to estimate the answers to the following questions by rounding.

1. CDs cost £4.95 each. Estimate (to the nearest pound) the cost of five CDs.
2. One pair of trainers is priced at £15.99. Another pair is priced at £12.95. What is the approximate difference in price (to the nearest pound)?
3. Cinema tickets are £2.10 each. Estimate to the nearest pound the cost of taking three friends with you for a birthday celebration.
4. A glass of milk is 290ml. To the nearest 100ml how much milk do you need for three glasses?
5. The length of your playground is 39 metres and the width is 23 metres. Use rounding to estimate the distance if you walk all the way round.
6. Look at the following calculation. Estimate by rounding to check whether you think it is correct: 63 + 81 = 144.
7. 142 − 71 = ? Round to the nearest 10 to estimate the answer.
8. Apples cost 23p each. Daniel says he paid less than £1 for four apples. Is he correct?
9. Pears cost 99p for a bag of five. What is the approximate cost of each pear?
10. Strawberries are £0.99 a box. Katy has £5 and she says she can buy only four boxes. Is this true or false?

Answers

1. £25
2. £3
3. £8
4. 900ml
5. 120 metres
6. 60 + 80 = 140 so it is correct
7. 140 − 70 = 70
8. Yes
9. 20p
10. False

38 Total 100

Resources
None

Learning objective
Use knowledge of addition and subtraction facts and place value to derive sums and differences of pairs of multiples of 10, 100 or 1000

Type of starter
Rehearse

Say each number, then pause (for example: *I say 70, you say ...*). On a silent signal from you, the children together say the other number of the pair to total 100.

1. 70	5. 72	9. 61	13. 58
2. 25	6. 40	10. 41	14. 14
3. 80	7. 10	11. 93	15. 66
4. 88	8. 65	12. 23	16. 27

Answers

1. 30	9. 39
2. 75	10. 59
3. 20	11. 7
4. 12	12. 77
5. 28	13. 42
6. 60	14. 86
7. 90	15. 34
8. 35	16. 73

39 Double number chains (2)

Resources
None

Learning objective
Identify the doubles of two-digit numbers; use these to calculate doubles of multiples of 10 and 100 and derive the corresponding halves

Type of starter
Rehearse

The children stand in a line or circle. The first child doubles the start number, which is doubled again by the next child, and so on. When a number greater than 100 is needed, that child sits down and is 'out' of the game. The game continues with a new start number.

1. 4	5. 10	9. 7
2. 13	6. 9	10. 17
3. 22	7. 15	
4. 3	8. 19	

Answers

1. 8, 16, 32, 64
2. 26, 52
3. 44, 88
4. 6, 12, 24, 48, 96
5. 20, 40, 80
6. 18, 36, 72
7. 30, 60
8. 38, 76
9. 14, 28, 56
10. 34, 68

40 Times tables facts

Learning objective
Derive and recall multiplication facts up to 10 × 10, the corresponding division facts and multiples of numbers to 10 up to the tenth multiple

Type of starter
Recall

Resources
None

Ask quick-fire questions. Children raise a hand to answer.

1. 4 × 3
2. 6 × 5
3. 8 × 2
4. 10 × 10
5. 8 × 4
6. 4 × 2
7. 6 × 10
8. 2 × 5
9. 8 × 3
10. 4 × 4
11. 1 × 10
12. 5 × 3
13. 6 × 2
14. 9 × 5
15. 6 × 4

Answers

1. 12
2. 30
3. 16
4. 100
5. 32
6. 8
7. 60
8. 10
9. 24
10. 16
11. 10
12. 15
13. 12
14. 45
15. 24

41 Describing 3D shapes

Learning objective
Visualise 3D objects from 2D drawings; make nets of common solids

Type of starter
Rehearse

Mental strategy
Visualising the shape as it is being described

Resources
3D shapes: cube, cuboid, hexagonal prism, sphere, square-based pyramid, triangular prism, triangular-based pyramid

Give one child a 3D shape (shapes 1–4) to hold behind their back and ask them to describe it to the rest of the class.

Now put 3D shapes (shapes 5–8) in a bag one at a time. Invite the children to ask questions about the shape to identify it.

1. Cube
2. Square-based pyramid
3. Cuboid
4. Triangular prism
5. Triangular-based pyramid
6. Hexagonal prism
7. Cuboid
8. Sphere

Answers

1. 6 faces, 6 vertices, 12 edges (all same length)
2. 5 faces, 5 vertices, 8 edges
3. 6 faces, 6 vertices, 12 edges (not all the same length)
4. 5 faces, 9 edges, 6 vertices
5. 4 faces, 4 vertices, 6 edges
6. 8 faces, 12 vertices, 18 edges
7. 6 faces, 6 vertices, 12 edges (not all the same length)
8. 1 face, no vertices, no edges, will roll

BLOCK C

Unit 1

100 Mental Maths Starters				100 Maths Lessons		
Page	Objective	Activity title	Starter type	Unit	Lesson	Page
36	Answer a question by identifying what data to collect; organise, present, analyse and interpret the data in tables, diagrams, tally charts, pictograms and bar charts, using ICT where appropriate	42 Interpreting the pictogram	Read	1	1	97
37	Answer a question by identifying what data to collect; organise, present, analyse and interpret the data in tables, diagrams, tally charts, pictograms and bar charts, using ICT where appropriate	43 Favourite season (bar chart)	Read	1	2	9
38	Choose and use standard metric units and their abbreviations when estimating, measuring and recording length, weight and capacity; know the meaning of 'kilo', 'centi' and 'milli' and, where appropriate, use decimal notation to record measurements (e.g. 1.3m or 0.6kg)	44 Body parts	Recall	1	7	101
39	Choose and use standard metric units and their abbreviations when estimating, measuring and recording length, weight and capacity; know the meaning of 'kilo', 'centi' and 'milli' and, where appropriate, use decimal notation to record measurements (e.g. 1.3m or 0.6kg)	45 Estimating length	Reason	1	8	102
40	Interpret intervals and divisions on partially numbered scales and record readings accurately, where appropriate to the nearest tenth of a unit	46 How much is in the jug?	Read	1	9	103
41	Interpret intervals and divisions on partially numbered scales and record readings accurately, where appropriate to the nearest tenth of a unit	47 It's near enough!	Reason	1	10	103

Unit 2

100 Mental Maths Starters				100 Maths Lessons		
Page	Objective	Activity title	Starter type	Unit	Lesson	Page
42	Suggest a line of enquiry and the strategy needed to follow it; collect, organise and interpret selected information to find answers	48 Traffic survey	Reason	2	2	108
43	Answer a question by identifying what data to collect; organise, present, analyse and interpret the data in tables, diagrams, tally charts, pictograms and bar charts, using ICT where appropriate	49 Save the birds	Recall	2	3	109

Unit 2 ...continued

100 Mental Maths Starters				100 Maths Lessons		
Page	Objective	Activity title	Starter type	Unit	Lesson	Page
44	Report solutions to puzzles and problems, giving explanations and reasoning orally and in writing, using diagrams and symbols	50 Favourite season	Read	2	5	110
45	Interpret intervals and divisions on partially numbered scales and record readings accurately, where appropriate to the nearest tenth of a unit	51 What's the division?	Reason	2	7	113
45	Choose and use standard metric units and their abbreviations when estimating, measuring and recording length, weight and capacity; know the meaning of 'kilo', 'centi' and 'milli' and, where appropriate, use decimal notation to record measurements (e.g. 1.3m or 0.6kg)	52 Metric conversion	Recall	2	8	114
46	Compare the impact of representations where scales have intervals of differing step size	53 How many kilograms?	Read	2	10	115

Unit 3

100 Mental Maths Starters				100 Maths Lessons		
Page	Objective	Activity title	Starter type	Unit	Lesson	Page
47	Report solutions to puzzles and problems, giving explanations and reasoning orally and in writing, using diagrams and symbols	54 Choosing and using charts and diagrams	Recall	3	3	121
48	Interpret intervals and divisions on partially numbered scales and record readings accurately, where appropriate to the nearest tenth of a unit	55 Hair colour	Rehearse	3	4	122
49	Answer a question by identifying what data to collect; organise, present, analyse and interpret the data in tables, diagrams, tally charts, pictograms and bar charts, using ICT where appropriate	56 Using Carroll diagrams	Read	3	5	123
49	Choose and use standard metric units and their abbreviations when estimating, measuring and recording length, weight and capacity; know the meaning of 'kilo', 'centi' and 'milli' and, where appropriate, use decimal notation to record measurements (e.g. 1.3m or 0.6kg)	57 Estimating	Rehearse	3	7	126
50	Suggest a line of enquiry and the strategy needed to follow it; collect, organise and interpret selected information to find answers	58 Selecting and presenting information	Reason	3	8	122
51	Compare the impact of representations where scales have intervals of differing step size	59 Measuring jugs	Refine	3	9	127

42 Interpreting the pictogram

Resources
Sticky notes; on the board: 'Favourite seasons' pictogram (see activity)

Learning objective
Answer a question by identifying what data to collect; organise, present, analyse and interpret the data in tables, diagrams, tally charts, pictograms and bar charts, using ICT where appropriate

Type of starter
Read

Mental strategy
Accurate counting, comparison and placing of sticky notes on pictogram to allow accurate interpretation

Answers

1. 20
2. Summer
3. Autumn
4. 5
5. Spring and winter

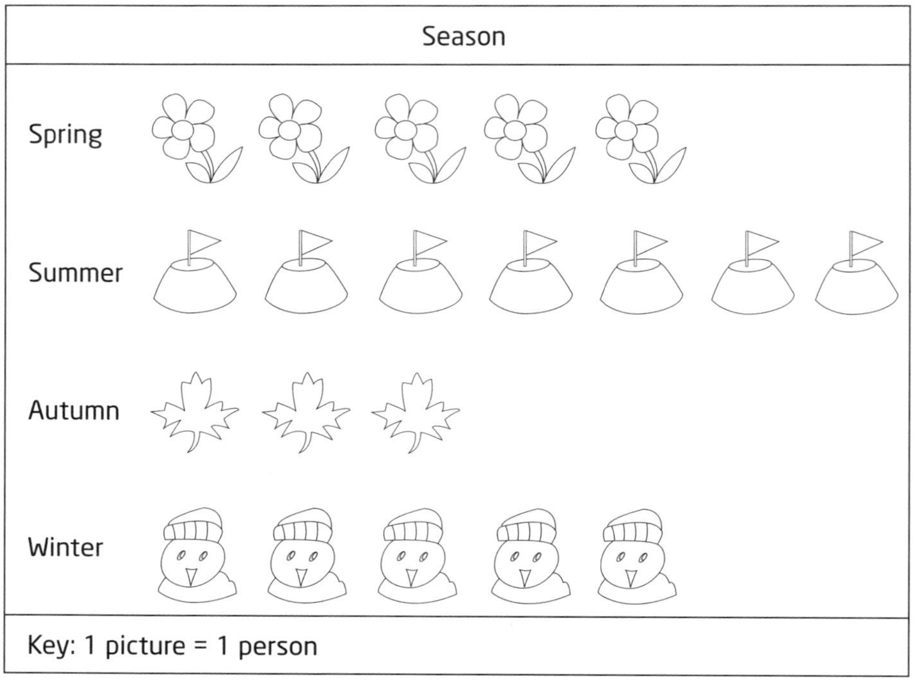

Ask the children to look at the pictogram, then answer these questions.

1. How many people completed the survey?
2. Which was the most popular season?
3. Which was the least popular season?
4. How many people liked winter the best?
5. Which two seasons had the same number of votes?

Now ask the children to complete a class survey on the same topic. Give each child a sticky note and ask them to write on it the name of their favourite season and its picture (flower, sandcastle, leaf, snowman). Invite them to stick their notes on the board to make a pictogram similar to the one already displayed.

43 Favourite season (bar chart)

Learning objective
Answer a question by identifying what data to collect; organise, present, analyse and interpret the data in tables, diagrams, tally charts, pictograms and bar charts, using ICT where appropriate

Type of starter
Read

Mental strategy
Accurate counting and comparison

Accurate interpretation of class bar chart

Resources
Data collected by the children in the previous activity on the class's favourite seasons; on interactive whiteboard: large blank bar chart

Tell the children that they are going to transfer the information from the previous 'sticky note' activity onto a bar chart. Explain that this can be a more permanent record of their findings. As you complete the bar chart together, ask:

1. Are we going to select a different colour for each season? Choose a colour for each.
2. How far must the line extend for spring?
3. How far must the line extend for summer?
4. How far must the line extend for autumn?
5. How far must the line extend for winter?

When the bar chart is complete, ask questions similar to those in the previous activity to assess how well the children can interpret their class bar chart. For example:

6. Which is the most popular season in our class?
7. Which is the least popular season in our class?
8. How many people like summer the best?
9. How many people like winter the best?
10. Which is more popular: spring or autumn?

No set answers

44 Body parts

Resources
On the board: the terms 'kilometre', 'metre', 'centimetre', 'millimetre', 'metric unit', 'standard unit'

Learning objective
Choose and use standard metric units and their abbreviations when estimating, measuring and recording length, weight and capacity; know the meaning of 'kilo', 'centi' and 'milli' and, where appropriate, use decimal notation to record measurements (e.g. 1.3m or 0.6kg)

Type of starter
Recall

Mental strategy
Using a small metric unit to measure objects with a short length

Using a larger metric unit to measure objects with a longer length

Answers
1. cm
2. mm or cm
3. cm
4. cm
5. m
6. 10 (accept 9 or 11)
7. 1 (accept 0.5–1)
8. So that everyone uses the same measurement; 1 metre is the same everywhere
9. Miles
10. Accept any longer than a finger's length

Recap the metric units displayed on the board. Recall the abbreviations for each one.

Ask children to choose a suitable metric unit that could be used to measure the following objects. They should give their answers in abbreviated form.

1. Hand span
2. Width of little finger
3. Length of leg
4. Your height
5. The total height of everyone in our class

Ask the children to estimate the following.

6. How many middle finger lengths make 1 metre?
7. How many of your leg lengths make a metre?
8. Why is it important to measure using a standard unit?
9. We could measure the distance to town in kilometres. What imperial measurement is also used?
10. Which part of your body is longer than your finger?

45 Estimating length

Learning objective
Choose and use standard metric units and their abbreviations when estimating, measuring and recording length, weight and capacity; know the meaning of 'kilo', 'centi' and 'milli' and, where appropriate, use decimal notation to record measurements (e.g. 1.3m or 0.6kg)

Type of starter
Reason

Mental strategy
Knowing the relationship and size of each metric unit

Choosing an appropriate unit

Comparing an object with known lengths to establish a suitable estimate

Resources
Metre rule (marked in centimetres); classroom objects for each group of four children (scissors, paper, book, ruler, eraser, CD)

Put the children in pairs and ask them to estimate the lengths of the following objects, choosing an appropriate metric unit in each case.

1. Length of a pair of scissors
2. Height of the classroom
3. Length of the cupboard
4. Width of a piece of paper
5. Length of a book
6. Width of a ruler
7. Depth of a ruler
8. Length of an eraser
9. Diameter of a CD
10. Length of the classroom window
11. Height of the board
12. Height of a house/building (visible from the window)
13. Distance to the school fence
14. Distance to a local village
15. Distance to a local church

Ask different pairs of children to measure the lengths, so the rest of the class can compare their estimates with the actual measurements.

No set answers

46 How much is in the jug?

Resources
ITP: Measuring cylinders

Learning objective
Interpret intervals and divisions on partially numbered scales and record readings accurately, where appropriate to the nearest tenth of a unit

Type of starter
Read

Mental strategy
Counting forwards in different steps

Using divisions on a scale to help you work out what is not shown

Use the ITP 'Measuring cylinders'. Set the maximum to 50 and the scale to 1. Fill the jug to 13ml.

Choose different children to answer the following questions orally.

1. How much liquid is in the jug?
2. I need 30ml. How much more do I need to pour in?

Change the maximum to 100 and the scale to 1. Fill the jug to 36ml.

3. How much liquid is in the jug?
4. If I add 20ml, how much liquid will there be then?

Change the scale to 5. Use the arrow to mark each of the following measurements. Ask: *How much liquid is in the jug?*

5. 42ml 6. 67ml 7. 35ml

Change the maximum to 500 and the scale to 10. Use the arrow to mark each of the following measurements. Ask: *How much liquid is in the jug?*

8. 730ml 9. 245ml 10. 875ml

Change the maximum to 1000 and the scale to 50. Use the arrow to mark each of the following measurements. Ask: *How much liquid is in the jug?*

11. 250ml 12. 600ml 13. 475ml

Answers
1. 13ml
2. 17ml
3. 36ml
4. 56ml
5. 42ml
6. 67ml
7. 35ml
8. 730ml
9. 245ml
10. 875ml
11. 250ml
12. 600ml
13. 475ml

47 It's near enough!

Learning objective
Interpret intervals and divisions on partially numbered scales and record readings accurately, where appropriate to the nearest tenth of a unit

Type of starter
Reason

Mental strategy
Knowing what each division means on a scale

Counting forwards accurately from a known number to an unmarked division

Resources
ITP: Measuring cylinders

This activity could be done in conjunction with the previous activity.

Use the ITP 'Measuring cylinders'. Set the maximum to 100 and the scale to 5. Point the arrow at 45. Ask different children to answer the following questions orally.

1. How much is in the jug?
2. How did you work that out?
3. What difference would it make if I said there was 40ml?
4. When could it matter that I used 40ml of liquid instead of 45ml?

Change the maximum to 500 and the scale to 25. Ask a child to point the arrow to 325ml. Ask the rest of the class the following questions.

5. Is he right? How do you know?
6. If he had put it here (350ml), what difference would there be?
7. How much is each division worth on this scale?
8. What would happen to a recipe if I used 350ml of liquid instead of 300ml?

Ask the children to work with a partner to think of three different times when it is important that capacity is measured accurately (for example: recipes, medicines, petrol, when selling drinks). List the children's suggestions on the board and discuss.

Answers
1. 45ml
2. There is a line halfway between 40 and 50, that is 45; *or*

   Each division is worth 5ml. 40 + 5 = 45ml
3. You would be short of 5ml of liquid
4. For medicine/ recipes (for example)
5. The arrow should be halfway between 300 and 350; each division is worth 25ml. 300 + 25 = 325ml
6. There would be 25ml more liquid
7. 25ml
8. It would be too runny/it wouldn't work

BLOCK C

48 Traffic survey

Resources
On the board: car colour survey results (see activity)

Learning objective
Suggest a line of enquiry and the strategy needed to follow it; collect, organise and interpret selected information to find answers

Type of starter
Reason

Mental strategy
Choosing an appropriate graph/chart to show information

Choosing an appropriate scale to show the large numbers

Answers
For example:

1. In a table/chart/graph
2. Each unit = 50 or 25
3. Frequency chart, bar chart/block graph, pictogram
4. Pie chart, line graph

Silver is the most popular car colour
A traffic survey has been done to find out the most popular car colour in our village.
There are 3500 people living in our village.
We found twelve main colours of car.
The minimum number of people with a car of any one colour was 230; the maximum number was 980.
How can we show our information, so it can be read and understood clearly and enable us to test the above statement?

Organise the children to work in groups of four and ask them to read the car colour survey results (see above) on the board. Ask them to work together to decide:

1. how they will display this information
2. what scale they will need to use
3. what types of table/graph might be appropriate
4. what types of table/chart/graph would not be appropriate.

Finish by sharing and discussing ideas.

Note: The children do not need to make a chart or graph.

49 Save the birds

Learning objective
Answer a question by identifying what data to collect; organise, present, analyse and interpret the data in tables, diagrams, tally charts, pictograms and bar charts, using ICT where appropriate

Type of starter
Recall

Mental strategy
Knowing one bag = £5

Using the 5-times table or counting in fives to work out answers quickly

Resources
On the board: charity money pictogram (see activity)

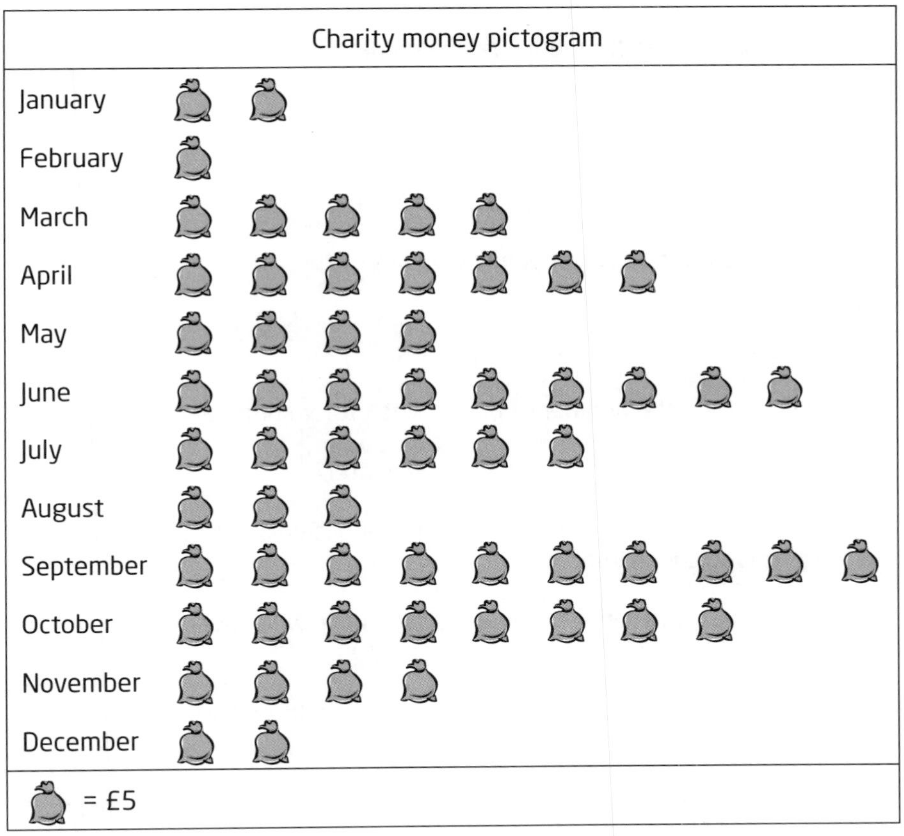

Explain that the pictogram shows money collected for a charity called Save the Birds during the last year. First establish that each bag is worth £5, then ask different children to tell you how much was collected in different months. Finally, ask:

1. In which month was the most money collected?
2. In which month was the least money collected?
3. How much more money was collected in April than August?
4. In which two months was only £10 collected?
5. What was the total sum collected in the first three months of the year?
6. If one bag = £5, how much would half a bag be worth?
7. If another half a bag had been collected in November, how much money would that have been?
8. How much less money was collected in March than June?

Answers
1. September
2. February
3. £20
4. January and December
5. £40
6. £2.50 (do not accept £2½)
7. £22.50 (do not accept £22½)
8. £20

50 Favourite season

Resources
ITP: Data handling; on the board: Frequency table

Favourite season	Frequency
Spring	53
Summer	95
Autumn	
Winter	54

Learning objective
Report solutions to puzzles and problems, giving explanations and reasoning orally and in writing, using diagrams and symbols

Type of starter
Read

Mental strategy
Accurate interpretation of data

Accurate mental addition, subtraction and checking answers using inverse operations

Show the children the frequency table you have drawn on the board (see 'Resources').

Explain that a survey has been done by a whole school of 250 pupils. Ask:

1. What data is missing from this chart?
2. Calculate the number of pupils who like autumn best.

Complete the chart, then enter the data into the ITP 'Data handling' and display it as a bar chart or block graph. Ask:

3. What is the total number of pupils who prefer spring and summer?
4. How many pupils prefer autumn and winter?
5. What is the difference between those pupils who chose Summer and those who chose Winter?
6. What is the difference between those pupils who chose spring and those who chose autumn?

Using the buttons on the ITP, view the data using the different presentation options.

7. How could the bar chart or block graph be enhanced to allow more accurate interpretation of the results?
8. Are the results what you would expect? Why or why not?

Answers
1. Number of pupils who prefer autumn
2. 48
3. 148
4. 102
5. 41
6. 5
7. Use of squared or lined paper
8. Yes/no with any reasonable explanation

51 What's the division?

Learning objective / Type of starter / Mental strategy	Resources
Learning objective Interpret intervals and divisions on partially numbered scales and record readings accurately, where appropriate to the nearest tenth of a unit **Type of starter** Reason **Mental strategy** Using an appropriate scale to work out an unmarked division	**Resources** A large counting stick, marked in tens but not labelled

Holding the counting stick horizontally or vertically as appropriate, point to both ends and establish their values. Then point to the appropriate division and ask: *How many kilograms/millilitres?* or *What is the temperature?*

Questions 1–5: ends represent 0kg and 20kg (divisions = 2kg)
Questions 6–10: ends represent 0ml and 50ml (divisions = 5ml)
Questions 11–15: ends represent −50° and 50° (divisions = 10°)

1. 14kg	2. 8kg	3. 10kg	4. 5kg	5. 12kg
6. 25ml	7. 30ml	8. 60ml	9. 75ml	10. 10ml
11. 20°	12. 35°	13. −10°	14. −40°	15. −25°

Answers
See questions

52 Metric conversion

Learning objective
Choose and use standard metric units and their abbreviations when estimating, measuring and recording length, weight and capacity; know the meaning of 'kilo', 'centi' and 'milli' and, where appropriate, use decimal notation to record measurements (e.g. 1.3m or 0.6kg)

Type of starter
Recall

Mental strategy
Knowing that 100cm = 1 metre

Knowing that 1000mm = 1 metre

Resources
On the board: large diagram:

65cm	6.5cm
50mm	3650cm
75cm	9mm
2500mm	27cm
360cm	25mm
8cm	820cm
7mm	32cm
840mm	9.5cm
0.5cm	92cm

Divide the class into two teams. Ask a child from each team in turn to convert one of the measurements in the diagram on the board into metres. They should write the correct conversion under the original measurement. The team with the most points wins.

Answers

0.65m	0.065m
0.05m	36.5m
0.75m	0.09m
2.5m	0.27m
3.6m	0.025m
0.08m	8.2m
0.007m	0.32m
0.84m	0.095m
0.05m	0.92m

53 How many kilograms?

Resources	
ITP: Measuring scales	**Learning objective** Compare the impact of representations where scales have intervals of differing step size **Type of starter** Read **Mental strategy** Counting forward from a known point Counting forward in steps of different sizes Using known numbers to work out unknown numbers

Answers

1-12. See questions
13. 150g
14. 75g
15. 90g
16. 5 × 100g, 2 × 10g and 1 × 5g
17. 3 × 100g, 1 × 50g and 3 × 10g

Use the ITP 'Measuring scales'. For each set of settings, use the clockwise arrow to point to the given masses. Ask: *How many kilograms?*

Set the maximum to 100 and the scale to 1; hide the pan.

1. 40kg 2. 65kg 3. 32kg 4. 16kg

Set the maximum to 200 and the scale to 10; hide the pan.

5. 50kg 6. 110kg 7. 140kg 8. 125kg

Set the maximum to 500 and the scale to 25; hide the pan.

9. 75kg 10. 225kg 11. 350kg 12. 475kg

Set the maximum to 500 and the scale to 25; show the pan. Put on one 100g and one 50g weight. Ask:

13. How much more do I need to put on to make 300g?
14. How much more do I need to put on to make 225g?
15. How much do I need to take off to make 60g?

Keeping the maximum at 500 and the scale at 25, show an empty pan. Ask:

16. Which weights do I need to put on to make 525g?
17. Which weights do I need to put on to make 380g?

54 Choosing and using charts and diagrams

Learning objective
Report solutions to puzzles and problems, giving explanations and reasoning orally and in writing, using diagrams and symbols

Type of starter
Recall

Resources
Examples of each of the following (blank): Venn diagram, frequency chart, tally chart, bar chart, pictogram, Carroll diagram

This is intended to be a purely oral activity for the purposes of group or class discussion and assessment.

Show the children each of the blank diagrams and charts. Ask:

1. Give an example of when you might use a tally chart.
2. What multiplication table is it useful to know when you use a tally chart?
3. How would you transfer information from the tally chart to a frequency chart?
4. If you wanted to report your findings about favourite food, so that others could quickly interpret them, which of the blank sheets shown would you use to present your results?
5. If you are asked to sort a set of regular and irregular 2D shapes into two categories (for example, lines of symmetry and no lines of symmetry) what kind of diagram would you use?
6. If you are asked to sort into categories that may overlap, what type of diagram should you use?
7. A Venn diagram is used for sorting even numbers and multiples of 5. Would I place 25 in the intersection? Why/why not?
8. Give three numbers that could be placed in the intersection.
9. If you were asked to find the ages of the boys and girls in your class (that is, how many 8-year-old girls/boys, how many 9-year-old girls/boys) what would be a suitable way of gathering and recording the information?
10. What would be a suitable diagram or chart to use for reporting the information on ages of the boys and girls in the class?

Answers

For example:

1. When you are carrying out a survey/gathering information.
2. 5-times table
3. Count the number of complete tallies and multiply by 5. Then add on the remaining single lines. Use the same categories for both charts.
4. A bar chart or a pictogram
5. Carroll diagram
6. Venn diagram
7. No. 25 is not an even number. It only belongs to the category 'multiples of 5'.
8. 10, 20, 30...
9. A tally chart and/or a frequency chart
10. Carroll diagram or bar chart

55 Hair colour

Resources
ITP: Data handling

Learning objective
Interpret intervals and divisions on partially numbered scales and record readings accurately, where appropriate to the nearest tenth of a unit

Type of starter
Rehearse

Mental strategy
Counting in fives

Counting on from a known number, to work out an unknown number

Answers

1. 30
2. 10
3. 16
4. 34
5. 5
6. 12
7. 16
8. White
9. Black
10. 46
11. 14
12. 7

Set up the following bar chart on the ITP 'Data handling'. Hide the values on the right-hand side.

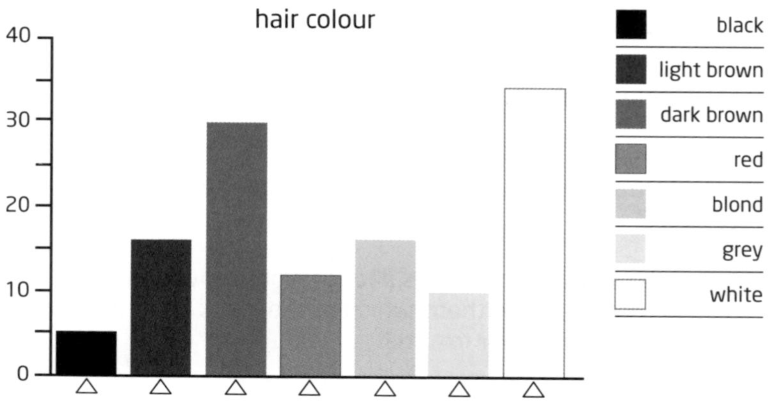

Put the children in pairs and ask them to answer the following questions.

1. How many people have dark brown hair?
2. How many people have grey hair?
3. How many people have light brown hair?
4. How many people have white hair?
5. How many people have black hair?
6. How many people have red hair?
7. How many people have blond hair?
8. Which is the most common hair colour?
9. Which is the least common hair colour?
10. What is the total number of people with brown hair?
11. How many more people have dark brown hair than light brown hair?
12. How many fewer people have black hair than red hair?

56 Using Carroll diagrams

Learning objective
Answer a question by identifying what data to collect; organise, present, analyse and interpret the data in tables, diagrams, tally charts, pictograms and bar charts, using ICT where appropriate

Type of starter
Read

Mental strategy
Use jottings and inverse operations to check answers

Resources
On the board: Carroll diagrams (see activity)

Ask the children to look at the Carroll diagrams on the board and answer questions about them, such as.

1. In the ages survey, how many children were questioned?
2. How many 8-year-olds were there?
3. How many boys were in the class? How many girls?
4. In the work or play survey, how many children were questioned?
5. How many fewer girls were surveyed than boys?
6. How many boys and girls preferred playtime?

	Age 8	Age 9
Girls	7	5
Boys	10	4

	Prefer playtime	Prefer being in class
Girls	21	36
Boys	41	40

Answers
1. 26
2. 17
3. 14, 12
4. 138
5. 24
6. 62

57 Estimating

Learning objective
Choose and use standard metric units and their abbreviations when estimating, measuring and recording length, weight and capacity; know the meaning of 'kilo', 'centi' and 'milli' and, where appropriate, use decimal notation to record measurements (e.g. 1.3m or 0.6kg)

Type of starter
Rehearse

Mental strategy
Ordering and comparing objects to give an idea of measurement

Resources
Three sets of objects, for example: (mass) 1kg bag of sugar, eraser, potato; (capacity) 1-litre bottle, yoghurt pot, watering can; (length) pencil sharpener, table, shoe

Show the children each set of objects, one set at a time. For each set, ask them to:

1. Order the objects (by mass, capacity or length, as appropriate), lowest to highest
2. Choose a suitable metric unit to measure each object
3. Choose a different object which you estimate would be about the same mass/capacity/length as one of the objects given (for example, an object which has the same mass as a bag of sugar).

Discuss the children's answers.

Answers
No set answers

58 Selecting and presenting information

Resources
On the board:
text passage (see activity)

Learning objective
Suggest a line of enquiry and the strategy needed to follow it; collect, organise and interpret selected information to find answers

Type of starter
Reason

Mental strategy
Using jottings to help select the relevant data

Answers

See answers below right

Learning preferences
There are 30 children in Class 4. There are 15 boys and 15 girls. In a class survey, one third of the boys said they preferred to read fiction whereas two thirds preferred non-fiction. Amongst the girls, 12 preferred fiction and 3 preferred non-fiction. In numeracy lessons, 5 boys preferred data handling to solving number problems. 10 boys preferred solving number problems to data handling. 7 girls preferred data handling and the rest of the girls preferred problem solving. 10 girls said they preferred literacy to numeracy but 10 boys said they preferred numeracy to literacy.

Divide the class into six groups. As you read the passage on the board, two of the groups should select the information on literacy or numeracy preference; two should select the relevant information on fiction or non-fiction preference; and the final two should select the relevant information on data handling or problem solving preference.

Share results, then ask each group to complete a Carroll diagram.

Finally, discuss whether the information is easier to interpret when presented visually in the form of a Carroll diagram.

Answers

	Fiction	Non-fiction
Girls	12	3
Boys	5	10

	Numeracy	Literacy
Girls	5	10
Boys	10	5

	Data handling	Problem solving
Girls	7	8
Boys	5	10

59 Measuring jugs

Learning objective Compare the impact of representations where scales have intervals of differing step size **Type of starter** Refine **Mental strategy** Working out the scale for each jug Counting up in steps of different sizes	**Resources** ITP: Measuring cylinder

Use the ITP 'Measuring cylinder'. Set the maximum to 50 and the scale to 1; hide the scale number. Set the red arrow to point at 29ml. Ask:

1. How many millilitres will this jug hold?
2. How much is each division worth?
3. Where is the red arrow pointing?

Change the maximum to 100ml and the scale to 1. Fill the jug to 38ml. Ask:

4. How much will the jug now hold?
5. How much is each division worth?
6. How much liquid is in the jug?
7. If I put another 12ml into the jug, how much will there be?

Change the maximum to 1000 and the scale to 20. Fill the jug to 460ml.

8. How much will the jug hold?
9. How much is each division worth?
10. How much liquid is in the jug?
11. I need 550ml. How much more liquid do I need to pour in?
12. I have used 120ml. How much is now left in the jug?

Change the scale to 50. Fill the jug to 350ml.

13. How much more liquid do I need to fill it to 1 litre?

Answers

1. 50ml
2. 1ml
3. 29ml
4. 100ml
5. 1ml
6. 38ml
7. 50ml
8. 1000ml
9. 20ml
10. 460ml
11. 90ml
12. 340ml
13. 650ml

BLOCK D

Unit 1

100 Mental Maths Starters				100 Maths Lessons		
Page	Objective	Activity title	Starter type	Unit	Lesson	Page
54	Add or subtract mentally pairs of two-digit whole numbers (e.g. 47 + 58, 91 – 35)	60 Clever one	Rehearse	1	2	132
54	Recognise horizontal and vertical lines; use the eight compass points to describe direction; describe and identify the position of a square on a grid of squares	61 Where am I?	Rehearse	1	3	132
55	Choose and use standard metric units and their abbreviations when estimating, measuring and recording length, weight and capacity; know the meaning of 'kilo', 'centi' and 'milli' and, where appropriate, use decimal notation to record measurements (e.g. 1.3m or 0.6kg)	62 What's my unit?	Read	1	5	134
56	Interpret intervals and divisions on partially numbered scales and record readings accurately, where appropriate to the nearest tenth of a unit	63 What's my number?	Refine	1	6	135
57	Read time to the nearest minute; use am, pm and 12-hour clock notation; choose units of time to measure time intervals; calculate time intervals from clocks and timetables	64 What time is it?	Refresh	1	8	137
58	Solve one-step and two-step problems involving numbers, money or measures, including time; choose and carry out appropriate calculations, using calculator methods where appropriate	65 Adding and subtracting money	Rehearse	1	9	137

Unit 2

100 Mental Maths Starters				100 Maths Lessons		
Page	Objective	Activity title	Starter type	Unit	Lesson	Page
59	Solve one-step and two-step problems involving numbers, money or measures, including time; choose and carry out appropriate calculations, using calculator methods where appropriate	66 Measurement problems	Rehearse	2	3	145
60	Derive and recall multiplication facts up to 10 × 10, the corresponding division facts and multiples of numbers to 10 up to the tenth multiple	67 Division quiz	Recall	2	5	147

BLOCK D

Unit 2 ...continued

100 Mental Maths Starters				100 Maths Lessons		
Page	Objective	Activity title	Starter type	Unit	Lesson	Page
61	Use decimal notation for tenths and hundredths and partition decimals; relate the notation to money and measurement; position one-place and two-place decimals on a number line	(68) What's the point?	Refresh	2	7	150
62	Choose and use standard metric units and their abbreviations when estimating, measuring and recording length, weight and capacity; know the meaning of 'kilo', 'centi' and 'milli' and use decimal notation to record measurements (e.g. 1.3m or 0.6kg)	(69) Abbreviations	Read	2	8	150
63	Choose and use standard metric units and their abbreviations when estimating, measuring and recording length, weight and capacity; know the meaning of 'kilo', 'centi' and 'milli' and use decimal notation to record measurements (e.g. 1.3m or 0.6kg)	(70) Change me!	Rehearse	2	9	151
64	Recognise horizontal and vertical lines; use the eight compass points to describe direction; describe and identify the position of a square on a grid of squares	(71) Directions	Refine	2	10	152

Unit 3

100 Mental Maths Starters				100 Maths Lessons		
Page	Objective	Activity title	Starter type	Unit	Lesson	Page
65	Solve one-step and two-step problems involving numbers, money or measures, including time; choose and carry out appropriate calculations, using calculator methods where appropriate	(72) Spending money	Rehearse	3	1	158
66	Use decimal notation for tenths and hundredths and partition decimals; relate the notation to money and measurement; position one-place and two-place decimals on a number line	(73) Multiplying and dividing by 10 or 100	Recall	3	2	158
66	Draw rectangles and measure and calculate their perimeters; find the area of rectilinear shapes drawn on a square grid by counting squares	(74) Perimeters	Recall	3	4	160
67	Know that angles are measured in degrees and that one whole turn is 360°; compare and order angles less than 180°	(75) Acute trouble	Refresh	3	6	162
67	Choose and use standard metric units and their abbreviations when estimating, measuring and recording length, weight and capacity; know the meaning of 'kilo', 'centi' and 'milli' and, where appropriate, use decimal notation to record measurements (e.g. 1.3m or 0.6kg)	(76) All change!	Recall	3	7	163
68	Read time to the nearest minute; use am, pm and 12-hour clock notation; choose units of time to measure time intervals; calculate time intervals from clocks and timetables	(77) How long?	Rehearse	3	10	165

60 Clever one

Resources
A board or flipchart

Learning objective
Add or subtract mentally pairs of two-digit whole numbers (e.g. 47 + 58, 91 – 35)

Type of starter
Rehearse

Answers

1.	45	7.	37
2.	67	8.	63
3.	41	9.	89
4.	56	10.	46
5.	79	11.	53
6.	55	12.	83

Write *25 + 19* and *33 + 21* on the board. Ask for the answers and strategies to find them. Emphasise the method of adding 20 (2 tens), then adjusting up or down as necessary.

Ask:

1.	26 + 19	5.	60 + 19	9.	68 + 21
2.	48 + 19	6.	34 + 21	10.	25 + 21
3.	22 + 19	7.	16 + 21	11.	24 + 29
4.	37 + 19	8.	42 + 21	12.	52 + 31

61 Where am I?

Resources
On the board:
Compass diagram:

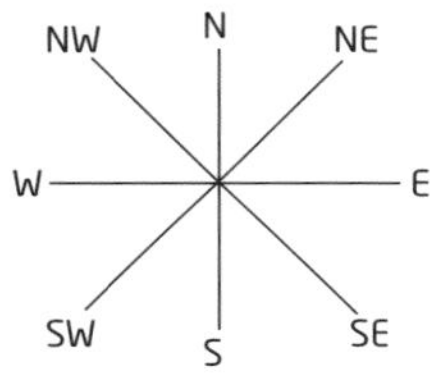

Learning objective
Recognise horizontal and vertical lines; use the eight compass points to describe direction; describe and identify the position of a square on a grid of squares

Type of starter
Rehearse

Mental strategy
Knowledge of eight points of compass – W and E (for West and East) spell WE

Understanding clockwise/anti-clockwise turns

Answers
1. East
2. North-east
3. South-east
4. South-west
5. West
6. North-west
7. North
8. South

Divide the class into eight groups and name each group after a point on the compass.

Read the following instructions. Ask the groups to stand up if the instruction ends at their compass point.

1. I am facing North and make quarter of a turn, clockwise.
2. I am facing South-west and make a half turn, anti-clockwise.
3. I am facing North-east and make a quarter turn, clockwise.
4. I am facing South-east and make a three-quarter turn, anti-clockwise.
5. I am facing South and make a three-quarter turn, anti-clockwise.
6. I am facing South-west and make a 90° turn, clockwise.
7. I am facing South and make a 180° turn, anti-clockwise.
8. I am facing South and turn through 360°.

62 What's my unit?

Learning objective
Choose and use standard metric units and their abbreviations when estimating, measuring and recording length, weight and capacity; know the meaning of 'kilo', 'centi' and 'milli' and, where appropriate, use decimal notation to record measurements (e.g. 1.3m or 0.6kg)

Type of starter
Read

Mental strategy
Knowing the abbreviations for units of measurement

Choosing the appropriate unit of measurement

Knowing that smaller objects need to be measured using a smaller unit of measurement

Resources
Piece of paper for each child; on the board: abbreviations table:

mm	cm
m	km
g	kg
ml	l

Start by reading the measurement abbreviations on the board and asking children for the matching words.

Ask the children to fold their pieces of paper into eight parts and label them with the measurement abbreviations (as on the board). They should then cut the paper into eight separate pieces and spread them out in front of them.

Explain that you will name an object and they should show you the card which shows the best unit to measure it with.

1. Length of your finger
2. Mass of a bag of potatoes
3. Liquid in a cup
4. Height of a tree
5. Mass of a pencil
6. Liquid in a watering can
7. Distance to your nearest town
8. Mass of a packet of butter
9. Liquid on a teaspoon
10. Length of the classroom
11. Mass of you
12. Width of a pen

Answers
1. cm
2. kg
3. ml
4. m
5. g
6. l
7. km
8. g
9. ml
10. m
11. kg
12. mm

63 What's my number?

Resources
Four blank number lines for each child (from photocopiable page 92)

Learning objective
Interpret intervals and divisions on partially numbered scales and record readings accurately, where appropriate to the nearest tenth of a unit

Type of starter
Refine

Mental strategy
Working out what each division on a scale is equal to

Answers
See answers below right

Ask the children to follow these instructions to label their number lines.

1. Label the first number line 0 on the left end and 20 on the right end.
2. Label the second number line 0 on the left end and 50 on the right end.
3. Label the third number line 0 on the left end and 100 on the right end.
4. Label the fourth number line −10 on the left end and +10 on the right end.

Now ask the children to mark and label the following numbers on their number lines.

5. First number line: 4, 8, 16 and 11
6. Second number line: 20, 35, 40 and 5
7. Third number line: 30, 50, 80 and 75
8. Fourth number line: 0, −2, +4, +6.

Ask the children how much each division is worth on each of their four lines.

Ask the children to look at the third number line and imagine it is 1 metre long. Ask them to use it help them write the following measurements in metres.

9. 30cm
10. 75cm

Answers

1-8

First number line (divisions are worth 2)

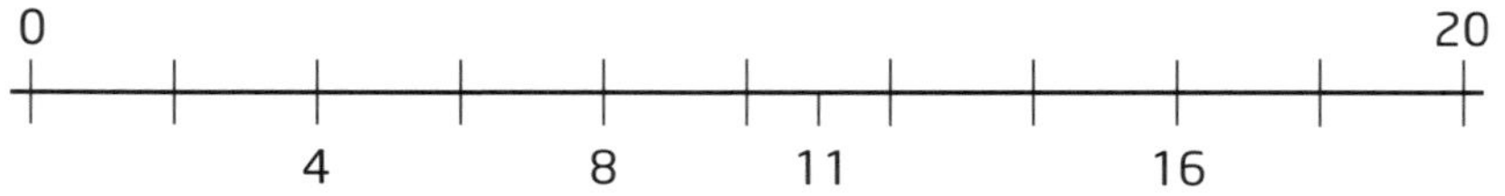

Second number line (divisions are worth 5)

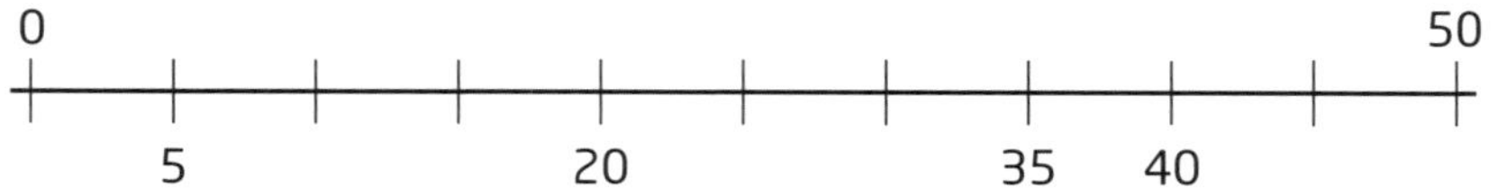

Third number line (divisions are worth 10)

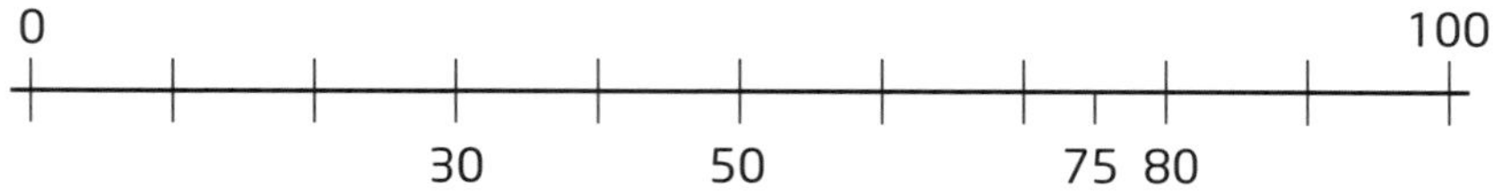

Fourth number line (divisions are worth 2)

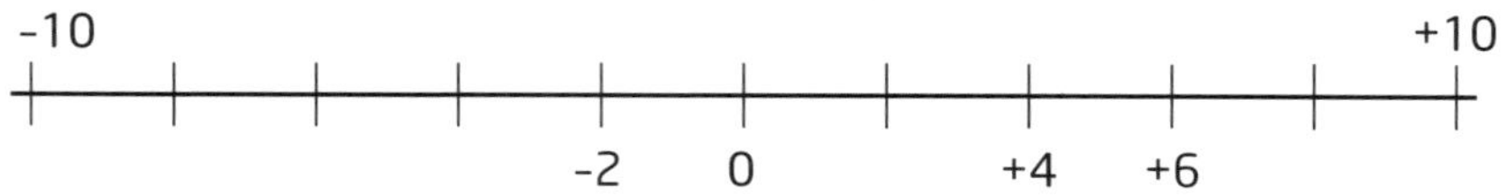

9. 0.3m
10. 0.75m

64 What time is it?

Learning objective
Read time to the nearest minute; use am, pm and 12-hour clock notation; choose units of time to measure time intervals; calculate time intervals from clocks and timetables

Type of starter
Refresh

Mental strategy
Knowing that the hour hand is the short hand and that the long hand measures minutes

Resources
Large analogue demonstration clock; individual pupil clocks

Use the demonstration clock to show children the following times. Ask them to write the time in digital form.

1. 2.30
2. 5.45
3. 11.05
4. 8.20
5. 12.55

Give the children a clock each. Ask them to show the following times.

6. 10.40
7. Five past 6
8. Half past 2
9. Quarter to 5
10. Twenty past four

Ask:

11. It is 9.15. Show me what time it will be in 40 minutes.
12. It is five past 1. Show me what the time will be in 20 minutes.

Answers
1-10. See questions
11. 9.55 (shown on clock)
12. 1.25 (shown on clock)

BLOCK D

65 Adding and subtracting money

Resources
None

Learning objective
Solve one-step and two-step problems involving numbers, money or measures, including time; choose and carry out appropriate calculations, using calculator methods where appropriate

Type of starter
Rehearse

Ask the children the following questions.

1. Add together 12p and 5p.
2. Take 8p from 20p.
3. Find the total of 8p and 11p.
4. I spent 9p and 6p. How much did I spend altogether?
5. How much change would you have from 20p if you spent 11p?
6. Add together 10p and 4p and take 7p from the answer.
7. You buy two pencils costing 8p each. How much change do you get from 20p?
8. I had 6p change from 20p. How much had I spent?
9. Take the total of 7p and 6p from 20p.
10. Add 14p and 5p and take away 7p.
11. Add together 10p, 5p and 2p and take 9p from the answer.
12. I have 8p change from three five-pence pieces. How much have I spent?
13. Take the total of 10p, 5p, 2p and 1p from 20p.
14. You buy two apples at 9p each. How much change do you get from 20p?
15. There were 125 pennies in a tin. How much more than £1 was this?

Answers

1. 17p
2. 12p
3. 19p
4. 15p
5. 9p
6. 7p
7. 4p
8. 14p
9. 7p
10. 12p
11. 8p
12. 7p
13. 2p
14. 2p
15. 25p

66 Measurement problems

Learning objective
Solve one-step and two-step problems involving numbers, money or measures, including time; choose and carry out appropriate calculations, using calculator methods where appropriate

Type of starter
Rehearse

Mental strategy
Converting each measurement to the smaller unit before doing the calculation

Converting the answer to the larger unit if necessary

Resources
None

Ask the following questions.

1. I have 1.3kg of flour. If I use 400g, how much will be left?
2. I am 1.2m tall. Jack is 40cm taller. How tall is he?
3. I have £3.75. I save another 60p. How much have I now?
4. It is 3.4km to town. I have already walked 800 metres. How much further do I need to walk?
5. I spend £4.20 on 60g of cheese. How much is that per gram?
6. If it takes me 2½ hours to walk 10km, how long will it take me to walk 1km?
7. I need 30 × 300ml cups of orange juice for the football team. How many litres of orange juice should I buy?
8. What fraction of £4 is 40p?
9. How many millimetres are there in 45 centimetres?
10. The length of a ribbon is 2m. I cut off 60cm and then another 80cm. How much do I have left?
11. Jack has 4 × 20p coins and 3 × 10p coins. He spends 12p. How much does he have left?
12. A square room has sides of 520cm. How many metres long is its perimeter?
13. I read for 45 minutes and then spend 20 minutes practising for my spelling test. How long was that, in hours and minutes?
14. I buy a comic for 75p and a book for £3.45. How much have I spent?
15. I need 400g flour to bake a loaf of bread. How many kilos of flour do I need for six loaves?

Answers
1. 900g
2. 1.6m
3. £4.35
4. 2.6km
5. 7p
6. ¼ hour (15 minutes)
7. 9 litres
8. $^1/_{10}$
9. 450mm
10. 60cm
11. 98p
12. 20.8m or 20m 80cm
12. 1 hour 5 minutes
13. £4.20
14. 2.4kg

67 Division quiz

Resources
None

Learning objective
Derive and recall multiplication facts up to 10 × 10, the corresponding division facts and multiples of numbers to 10 up to the tenth multiple

Type of starter
Recall

Answers

1. 6
2. 3
3. 4
4. 9
5. 9
6. 7
7. 9
8. 7
9. 10
10. 8
11. 4
12. 6
13. 7
14. 8
15. 5

Remind the children that the 'quotient' is the result of one number being divided by another. Then ask the following questions.

1. How many twos in 12?
2. Share 15 among 5.
3. 40 divided by 10.
4. What is the quotient of 90 and 10?
5. What is half of 18?
6. Share 35 among 5.
7. What is the quotient of 45 and 5?
8. How many twos in 14?
9. 20 divided by 2.
10. How many groups of 5 can I make out of 40?
11. 8 divided by 2.
12. 30 divided by 5.
13. Share 70 among 10.
14. What is half of 16?
15. How many fives in 25?

68 What's the point?

Learning objective
Use decimal notation for tenths and hundredths and partition decimals; relate the notation to money and measurement; position one-place and two-place decimals on a number line

Type of starter
Refresh

Mental strategy
Knowing that the decimal point moves to the right when dividing by 10

Knowing the value of each digit in a decimal

Resources
Set of 1-9 numeral cards (from photocopiable page 89) for each group of six children

Divide the class into groups of six and give each group a set of 1-9 number cards.

Ask each child, in turn, to take two cards and make a two-digit number with them. Then ask them to divide their number by 10, to create a decimal.

Now ask each group to work together to order their decimals (from low to high).

Next, ask the children to divide their decimals by 10 again, to create a two-place decimal.

Finally, ask each group to order their two-place decimals.

No set answers

69 Abbreviations

Resources
On the board: table with space to write three objects in each section:

mm	cm
m	km

Learning objective
Choose and use standard metric units and their abbreviations when estimating, measuring and recording length, weight and capacity; know the meaning of 'kilo', 'centi' and 'milli' and, where appropriate, use decimal notation to record measurements (e.g. 1.3m or 0.6kg)

Type of starter
Read

Answers
1–4 see questions
5. cm
6. km
7. m
8. mm

Start by asking the children what each of the abbreviations shown on the board stand for, then ask them to spell the following.

1. millimetres
2. centimetres
3. metres
4. kilometres

Now ask children what unit they would use to measure the following.

1. Length of a cat
2. Distance to London
3. Height of the room
4. Width of an eraser

Finally, ask the children to copy the diagram on the board onto a piece of paper. Divide the children into groups of three or four and ask them to write three objects (or distances) that each particular measurement would be suitable for in each section.

Share the children's answers and discuss the appropriateness of their choices.

70 Change me!

Learning objective
Choose and use standard metric units and their abbreviations when estimating, measuring and recording length, weight and capacity; know the meaning of 'kilo', 'centi' and 'milli' and, where appropriate, use decimal notation to record measurements (e.g. 1.3m or 0.6kg)

Type of starter
Rehearse

Mental strategy
Knowing the relationship between millimetres, centimetres, metres and kilometres

Being able to multiply/divide by 10 or multiples of 10 to convert to the appropriate unit

Resources
None

Ask the following questions.

How many:

1. millimetres in a metre?
2. centimetres in a kilometre?
3. metres in a kilometre?
4. millimetres in a centimetre?
5. centimetres in a metre?
6. millimetres in a kilometre?

Change these measurements.

7. 1.6km to metres
8. 25.2m to centimetres
9. 0.6m to millimetres
10. 463cm to metres
11. 25mm to centimetres

Find two ways to write these measurements.

12. 4.2km
13. 3700mm
14. 0.6m
15. 78cm
16. 6850m

Answers

1. 1000
2. 100,000
3. 1000
4. 10
5. 100
6. 1,000,000
7. 1600m
8. 2520cm
9. 600mm
10. 4.63m
11. 2.5cm

Any two for each of the following:

12. 4200m, 420,000cm, 4,200,000mm
13. 370cm, 3.7m, 0.0037km
14. 0.0006km, 60cm, 600mm
15. 780mm, 0.78m, 0.00078km
16. 6.85km, 685,000cm, 6,850,000mm

71 Directions

Resources
ITP: Fixing points

Learning objective
Recognise horizontal and vertical lines; use the eight compass points to describe direction; describe and identify the position of a square on a grid of squares

Type of starter
Refine

Mental strategy
Knowing points of a compass

Knowing the difference between horizontal and vertical

Use the ITP 'Fixing points'. Choose a 5 × 5 grid and enable the line tool.

Remind the children of the eight points of the compass and their positions.

Draw each line turn (starting with A to B) and ask each question in turn.

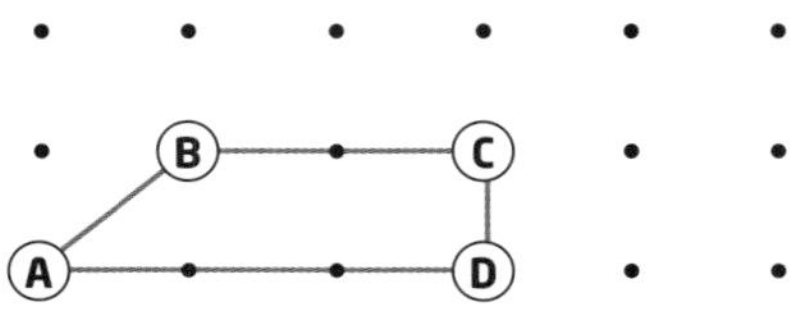

1. What is the direction from A to B?
2. What direction is it from B to C? Is BC a horizontal or vertical line?
3. What direction is it from C to D? Is CD a horizontal or vertical line?
4. What direction is it from D to A? Is DA a horizontal or vertical line?

Reset the screen and start the next diagram. Draw each line and ask question 5 before moving on to the next one, ending with the direction from E to A.

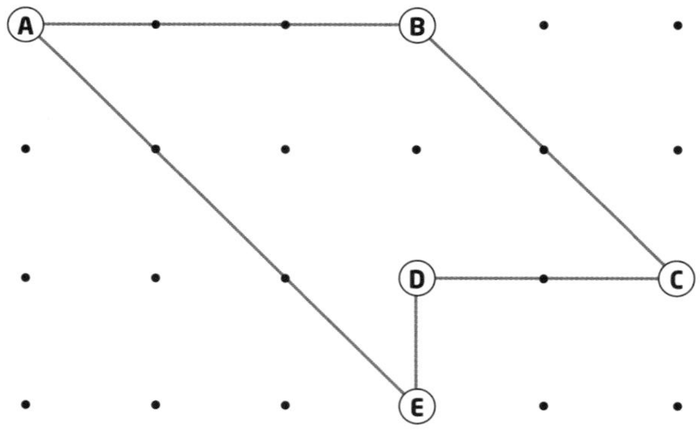

5. What direction is it from ... to ...?
6. Which lines are horizontal?
7. How many vertical lines are there?
8. If I start at A and go round the diagram in an anticlockwise direction, which line goes in a North-westerly direction?

Answers
1. North-east
2. East, horizontal
3. South, vertical
4. West, horizontal
5. AB East, BC South-east, CD West, DE South, EA North-west
6. AB, CD
7. One (DE)
8. CB

(72) **Spending money**

Learning objective	**Resources**
Solve one-step and two-step problems involving numbers, money or measures, including time; choose and carry out appropriate calculations, using calculator methods where appropriate	None

Type of starter
Rehearse

Mental strategy
Breaking the problem into parts

Knowing which operation to use to solve each part

Ask the following questions.

1. I have a £2 coin, a 50p, 2 × 20p, and 3 × 5p. How much money have I?

2. I save 60p a week for 8 weeks. How much have I saved?

3. I get £2 spending money each week. I buy a comic for 65p and some stickers for £1.10. How much will I have left?

4. I go to the pictures with two friends. We buy tickets for £2.25 each and one tub of popcorn for 90p. How much do we spend altogether?

5. I have £5. I buy my mum some flowers for her birthday at £2.99. How much do I have left for a card?

6. I want to buy a computer game for £26. If I save £3 a week, how many weeks will it take me before I have enough money to buy the game?

7. A mobile phone contract costs £15 per month. How much is this over 12 months?

8. I buy a bag of ten packets of crisps for £1.65. How much are they for each packet?

9. I have made 30 buns which I am going to sell to make money for charity. If I charge 8p for each bun, how much will I make?

10. Five pencils cost me 60p. How much would it cost me for 12 pencils?

11. Last year I bought a computer game for £24. Now it is double that price. How much is it now?

12. It costs me £1.84 for a return bus journey into town. How much would a single cost me?

13. I have £1.73. List the fewest coins I could have.

14. I get £1.75 spending money a week, but my friend gets £2.40. How much more money does she get than me?

15. When I go to France one euro = £1.10. If I buy something for 5 euros, how much is that in £s and pence?

Answers

1. £3.05
2. £4.80
3. 25p
4. £7.65
5. £2.01
6. Nine
7. £180
8. 16.5p
9. £2.40
10. £1.44
11. £48
12. 92p
13. £1, 50p, 20p, 2p, 1p
14. 65p
15. £5.50

73 Multiplying and dividing by 10 or 100

Resources
None

Learning objective
Use decimal notation for tenths and hundredths and partition decimals; relate the notation to money and measurement; position one-place and two-place decimals on a number line

Type of starter
Recall

Mental strategy
When dividing by 10, the decimal point moves one place to the left
When dividing by 100, the decimal point move two places to the left
When multiplying by 10, the decimal point moves one place to the right
When multiplying by 100, the decimal point moves two places to the right

Answers

1. 4.5
2. 67.4
3. 240m
4. 87.5
5. 250mm
6. £1.60
7. 0.032
8. 7.5
9. 0.0025
10. 36.2p
11. 5ml
12. 475
13. 30
14. 814
15. £37

Ask the following quick-fire questions.

1. 45 ÷ 10
2. 674 ÷ 10
3. 2400m ÷ 10
4. 8.75 × 10
5. 25mm × 10
6. 16p × 10
7. 3.2 ÷ 100
8. 750 ÷ 100
9. 0.25 ÷ 100
10. £36.20 ÷ 100
11. 500ml ÷ 100
12. 4.75 × 100
13. 0.3 × 100
14. 8.14 × 100
15. 37p × 100

74 Perimeters

Resources
On the board: a large diagram of a rectangle; one set of 1-9 numeral cards (from photocopiable page 89) for each pair

Learning objective
Draw rectangles and measure and calculate their perimeters; find the area of rectilinear shapes drawn on a square grid by counting squares

Type of starter
Recall

Mental strategy
Finding the perimeter of a rectangle by doubling each of the opposite sides and adding both totals

No set answers

Ask the children to work in pairs. Explain that they will be working out the perimeter of some rectangles. Each child takes two 1-9 numeral cards and uses these to make a two-digit number. Each two-digit number will be the measurement, in centimetres, for one of the sides of the rectangle. Ask each pair to double their numbers (to work out the length of the two opposite sides) and then add their totals together, to work out the total perimeter. Repeat.

75 Acute trouble

Learning objective
Know that angles are measured in degrees and that one whole turn is 360°; compare and order angles less than 180°

Type of starter
Refresh

Mental strategy
Recognising a right angle

Recognising an acute angle or angles less than 90°

Recognising an obtuse angle or angles more than 90°

Resources
ITP: Fixing points

Use the ITP 'Fixing points' to create an angle ABC. Explain to the children that, if the angle at B is less than a right angle, they should put their hands on their heads. If it is more than a right angle they should fold their arms. If they see a right angle they should stand up.

Change the size of the angle by dragging any of the points A, B or C to a different point. Give examples of acute, obtuse and right angles in rapid succession.

No set answers

76 All change!

Learning objective
Choose and use standard metric units and their abbreviations when estimating, measuring and recording length, weight and capacity; know the meaning of 'kilo', 'centi' and 'milli' and, where appropriate, use decimal notation to record measurements (e.g. 1.3m or 0.6kg)

Type of starter
Recall

Mental strategy
Knowing the relationships between different units of measurement

Resources
On the board: table of measurement abbreviations:

mm	g	ml
cm	kg (kilo)	l
m		
km		

Use the table on the board to help the children recall the different units of measurement for length, weight and capacity and rehearse the relationships between them.

Give a measurement (for example: 400cm) and say: *smaller/larger*. Choose a child to change the unit of length, and give a measurement which is smaller or larger (for example, a length greater than 4m, in metres or kilometres).

Choose different children at random, saying *smaller/larger* each time.

Repeat the activity, using weight and capacity starting measurements.

No set answers

77 How long?

Resources	Learning objective
On the board: large analogue clock	Read time to the nearest minute; use am, pm and 12-hour clock notation; choose units of time to measure time intervals; calculate time intervals from clocks and timetables **Type of starter** Rehearse **Mental strategy** Knowing the relationship between units of time Counting forwards/backwards in minutes or hours

Answers

1. 15 minutes
2. 1 hour 35 minutes (95 minutes)
3. 10.05
4. 5am or 05.00
5. 12.20
6. 1 minute 40 seconds
7. 5 hours 20 minutes
8. 2022
9. 4 weeks
10. Thursday
11. 9 hours 30 minutes
12. 8 hours 55 minutes
13. 5.10pm
14. 1 hour 45 minutes
15. 27 days (including 29th November and 25th December)

Ask the following questions.

1. I leave home at 8.25 and arrive at school and 8.40. How long did my journey take?
2. If the bus leaves town at 1.55 and arrives in our village at 3.30, how long was the journey?
3. We spend 50 minutes a day on numeracy. If we start our lesson at 9.15, what time will we finish it?
4. What time is it 8 hours after 9pm?
5. It is 11.35. What time will it be in 45 minutes?
6. A mental test has 20 questions, with five seconds each to answer them. How long is that in minutes?
7. A television series has eight programmes which last for 40 minutes each. How long is that in hours and minutes?
8. I am eight years old in 2009. What year will it be when I am 21?
9. It is 2nd March. The new Harry Potter film will be released on 30th March. How many weeks will I have to wait before I can see it?
10. The 3rd February is a Tuesday. What day will the 19th February be?
11. It is 9pm. I am going to bake a loaf of bread overnight. I want it to be ready for 6.30am. How many hours do I need to set the timer for?
12. I leave home at 4.20am. I fly to Majorca and arrive in my hotel at 1.15pm. How long has the journey taken me?
13. My flight for Heathrow takes off at 8.10pm. It takes me an hour to get to the airport. I have to be at the airport two hours before take-off. What time should I leave home?
14. A parcel should have been delivered before 1pm. It arrived at 2.45pm. How late was it?
15. It is 29th November. How many days is it until Christmas Day?

BLOCK E

Unit 1

100 Mental Maths Starters				100 Maths Lessons		
Page	**Objective**	**Activity title**	**Starter type**	**Unit**	**Lesson**	**Page**
71	Derive and recall multiplication facts up to 10 × 10, the corresponding division facts and multiples of numbers to 10 up to the tenth multiple	78 Tables bingo (2, 3, 4, 5, 10)	Recall	1	3	173
72	Derive and recall multiplication facts up to 10 × 10, the corresponding division facts and multiples of numbers to 10 up to the tenth multiple	79 Equation game	Refresh	1	4	174
72	Use diagrams to identify equivalent fractions (e.g. $^6/_8$ and $^3/_4$, or $^{70}/_{100}$ and $^7/_{10}$); interpret mixed numbers and position them on a number line (e.g. $3^1/_2$)	80 Fraction steps	Rehearse	1	7	176
73	Recognise the equivalence between decimal and fraction forms of one half, quarters, tenths and hundredths	81 Decimal and fraction twins	Refresh	1	8	176
73	Identify pairs of fractions that total 1	82 Pair them up!	Refresh	1	9	177
74	Recognise the equivalence between decimal and fraction forms of one half, quarters, tenths and hundredths	83 Fraction and decimal quiz	Recall	1	10	178
75	Find fractions of numbers, quantities or shapes (e.g. $^1/_5$ of 30 plums, $^3/_8$ of a 6 by 4 rectangle)	84 Half time	Rehearse	1	11	179
76	Find fractions of numbers, quantities or shapes (e.g. $^1/_5$ of 30 plums, $^3/_8$ of a 6 by 4 rectangle)	85 Shading shapes	Refresh	1	12	179

Unit 2

100 Mental Maths Starters				100 Maths Lessons		
Page	**Objective**	**Activity title**	**Starter type**	**Unit**	**Lesson**	**Page**
77	Choose and carry out appropriate calculations, using calculator methods where appropriate	86 Which operation?	Reason	2	2	190
77	Derive and recall multiplication facts up to 10 × 10, the corresponding division facts and multiples of numbers to 10 up to the tenth multiple	87 Multiplication clock	Recall	2	3	191
78	Derive and recall multiplication facts up to 10 × 10, the corresponding division facts and multiples of numbers to 10 up to the tenth multiple	88 Tables bingo (6, 7, 8, 9)	Recall	2	4	192

Unit 2 ...continued

100 Mental Maths Starters				100 Maths Lessons		
Page	**Objective**	**Activity title**	**Starter type**	**Unit**	**Lesson**	**Page**
79	Use diagrams to identify equivalent fractions (e.g. $^{6}/_{8}$ and $^{3}/_{4}$, or $^{70}/_{100}$ and $^{7}/_{10}$); interpret mixed numbers and position them on a number line (e.g. $3^{1}/_{2}$)	89 Mixed numbers	Rehearse	2	8	196
79	Find fractions of numbers, quantities or shapes (e.g. $^{1}/_{5}$ of 30 plums, $^{3}/_{8}$ of a 6 by 4 rectangle)	90 Half number chains	Recall	2	9	196
80	Find fractions of numbers, quantities or shapes (e.g. $^{1}/_{5}$ of 30 plums, $^{3}/_{8}$ of a 6 by 4 rectangle)	91 What's my value?	Refresh	2	10	197
81	Recognise the equivalence between decimal and fraction forms of one half, quarters, tenths and hundredths	92 Match the equal values (1)	Rehearse	2	13	199
81	Identify pairs of fractions that total 1	93 Match the pairs	Reason	2	15	200

Unit 3

100 Mental Maths Starters				100 Maths Lessons		
Page	**Objective**	**Activity title**	**Starter type**	**Unit**	**Lesson**	**Page**
82	Derive and recall multiplication facts up to 10 × 10, the corresponding division facts and multiples of numbers to 10 up to the tenth multiple	94 Division snap	Recall	3	2	208
82	Recognise the equivalence between decimal and fraction forms of one half, quarters, tenths and hundredths	95 Match the equal values (2)	Recall	3	8	215
83	Find fractions of numbers, quantities or shapes (e.g. $^{1}/_{5}$ of 30 plums, $^{3}/_{8}$ of a 6 by 4 rectangle)	96 Fractions of shapes	Refresh	3	9	215
84	Recognise the equivalence between decimal and fraction forms of one half, quarters, tenths and hundredths	97 More fractions	Rehearse	3	10	216
84	Use diagrams to identify equivalent fractions (e.g. $^{6}/_{8}$ and $^{3}/_{4}$, or $^{70}/_{100}$ and $^{7}/_{10}$); interpret mixed numbers and position them on a number line (e.g. $3^{1}/_{2}$)	98 Counting in quarters	Rehearse	3	11	216
85	Find fractions of numbers, quantities or shapes (e.g. $^{1}/_{5}$ of 30 plums, $^{3}/_{8}$ of a 6 by 4 rectangle)	99 Fraction search	Refresh	3	12	217
86	Use the vocabulary of ratio and proportion to describe the relationship between two quantities estimate a proportion	100 Problems of proportion (1)	Reason	3	14	218
86	Use the vocabulary of ratio and proportion to describe the relationship between two quantities estimate a proportion	101 Problems of proportion (2)	Refine	3	15	219

78 Tables bingo (2, 3, 4, 5, 10)

Learning objective
Derive and recall multiplication facts up to 10 × 10, the corresponding division facts and multiples of numbers to 10 up to the tenth multiple

Type of starter
Recall

Resources
Paper and a pencil for each child

Ask the children to choose eight multiples of 2, 3, 4, 5 and/or 10 and write them spread out on their paper.

Read out the questions. If the children have the answer to a question on their paper, they cross it out. The first child to cross out all eight numbers wins.

Repeat, using the questions in a different order.

1. 9 × 3
2. 10 × 5
3. 2 × 10
4. 2 × 3
5. 8 × 3
6. 2 × 4
7. 10 × 10
8. 9 × 4
9. 1 × 5
10. 10 × 3
11. 7 × 3
12. 1 × 2
13. 5 × 5
14. 8 × 4
15. 10 × 7
16. 3 × 3
17. 7 × 4
18. 6 × 10
19. 3 × 4
20. 8 × 10
21. 4 × 4
22. 5 × 2
23. 8 × 5
24. 7 × 2
25. 9 × 5
26. 1 × 3
27. 9 × 10
28. 3 × 5
29. 1 × 4
30. 7 × 5

Answers

1. 27
2. 50
3. 20
4. 6
5. 24
6. 8
7. 100
8. 36
9. 5
10. 30
11. 21
12. 2
13. 25
14. 32
15. 70
16. 9
17. 28
18. 60
19. 12
20. 80
21. 16
22. 10
23. 40
24. 14
25. 45
26. 3
27. 90
28. 15
29. 4
30. 35

79 Equation game

Resources
None

Learning objective
Derive and recall multiplication facts up to 10 ×10, the corresponding division facts and multiples of numbers to 10 up to the tenth multiple

Type of starter
Refresh

No set answers

Write *4 × 3 = 12* on the board. Ask for an equivalent multiplication statement (one with the same answer). For example: 6 × 2 = 12, 1 × 12 = 12, 3 × 4 = 12.

Now ask the children to find equivalent multiplication statements to:

1.	4 × 4 = 16	5.	6 × 3 = 18	9.	5 × 10 = 50
2.	10 × 3 = 30	6.	10 × 4 = 40	10.	50 × 2 = 100
3.	10 × 2 = 20	7.	5 × 2 = 10	11.	2 × 16 = 32
4.	3 × 4 = 12	8.	6 × 4 = 24	12.	7 × 10 = 70

80 Fraction steps

Resources
None

Learning objective
Use diagrams to identify equivalent fractions (e.g. $^6/_8$ and $^3/_4$, or $^{70}/_{100}$ and $^7/_{10}$); interpret mixed numbers and position them on a number line (e.g. $3^1/_2$)

Type of starter
Rehearse

Answers

1. 2½
2. 7
3. 4½
4. 20
5. 5¼
6. 7¾
7. 12½
8. 15
9. 14½
10. 18½
11. 10
12. 17

Count together in halves, then quarters up to 20. Remind the children that $^2/_4 = {}^1/_2$.

For questions 1-4, ask: *When we count in halves, what comes next after...?*

For questions 5-8, ask: *What comes next when we count in quarters?*

For questions 9-12, give the start number and the instruction.

1.	2	5.	5	9.	15, take off ½
2.	6½	6.	7½	10.	18¼, add ¼
3.	4	7.	12¼	11.	10½, take off ½
4.	19½	8.	14¾	12.	16¾, add ¼

81 Decimal and fraction twins

Learning objective
Recognise the equivalence between decimal and fraction forms of one half, quarters, tenths and hundredths

Type of starter
Refresh

Mental strategy
Remembering that the first digit after the decimal point represents tenths and the second digit represents hundredths

Remembering that one half = five tenths, one quarter = twenty-five hundredths, three quarters = seventy-five hundredths

Resources
Individual whiteboards

Write on the board (or say) the following numbers.

For questions 1-8, ask the children to write or say the equivalent decimal. For questions 9-16, ask them to write or say the equivalent fraction or mixed number:

1. ½	5. $^1/_{100}$	9. 0.25	13. 0.7
2. ¼	6. $^7/_{100}$	10. 0.75	14. 3.1
3. $^3/_{10}$	7. $^{49}/_{100}$	11. 0.5	15. 5.5
4. $^9/_{10}$	8. $^{80}/_{100}$	12. 0.05	16. 19.75

Answers

1. 0.5	9. ¼
2. 0.25	10. ¾
3. 0.3	11. ½
4. 0.9	12. $^5/_{100}$
5. 0.01	13. $^7/_{10}$
6. 0.07	14. $3^1/_{10}$
7. 0.49	15. 5½
8. 0.80	16. 19¾

82 Pair them up!

Learning objective
Identify pairs of fractions that total 1

Type of starter
Refresh

Mental strategy
Finding fractions that total 1 by looking for denominators that are the same, then numerators that add up to the denominator exactly

Resources
Individual whiteboards

Write the fractions below on the board and ask the children to pair them up so that each pair makes a total of 1.

1-4. $^2/_6$ $^1/_8$ $^3/_5$ $^4/_6$ $^4/_{10}$ $^7/_8$ $^6/_{10}$ $^2/_5$

Now ask the children to write the fraction that must be added to make 1.

5. $^5/_6$ + ? =1	8. $^5/_8$ + ? = 1	11. ¼ + ? = 1
6. $^2/_3$ + ? = 1	9. $^1/_{10}$ + ? = 1	12. $^3/_{16}$ + ? = 1
7. ¾ + ? = 1	10. ½ + ? = 1	

Answers

1. $^2/_6$ and $^4/_6$
2. $^1/_8$ and $^7/_8$
3. $^3/_5$ and $^2/_5$
4. $^4/_{10}$ and $^6/_{10}$

5. $^1/_6$	6. $^1/_3$
7. ¼	8. $^3/_8$
9. $^9/_{10}$	10. ½
11. ¾	12. $^{13}/_{16}$

83 Fraction and decimal quiz

Resources
On the board: 0–1 number line marked in decimals; individual whiteboards

Learning objective
Recognise the equivalence between decimal and fraction forms of one half, quarters, tenths and hundredths

Type of starter
Recall

Mental strategy
Remembering that $^1/_{10}$ = 0.1, and so on

Answers
1. 0.3
2. 0.4
3. 0.9
4. 0.5
5. 0.3
6. 1.0
7. 0.1
8. 0.3
9. 0.4
10. 0.1
11. 0.5
12. 0.25
13. 0.75
14. 0.75
15. 0.5

Display the number line on the board. Read out the following calculations. Children should write their answers on their whiteboards as decimals.

1. 0.2 add one tenth
2. 0.1 add three tenths
3. 0.5 add four tenths
4. 0.6 subtract one tenth
5. 0.6 subtract three tenths
6. 0.9 add one tenth
7. 0.3 subtract two tenths
8. 0.8 subtract five tenths
9. 0.7 subtract three tenths
10. 1.0 subtract nine tenths
11. Write one half as a decimal
12. Write one quarter as a decimal
13. Write three quarters as a decimal
14. Add ¼ and ½ and write the answer as a decimal
15. Add ¼ and ¼ and write the answer as a decimal

84 Half time

Learning objective
Find fractions of numbers, quantities or shapes (e.g. $^1/_5$ of 30 plums, $^3/_8$ of a 6 by 4 rectangle)

Type of starter
Rehearse

Resources
A board or flipchart

Write *half of 25* = on the board. Ask for the answer and strategies to find it. Encourage a rapid pace.

Emphasise that an odd number halved will always give a fraction.

Ask the children to find the following:

1. Half of 16
2. Half of 17
3. Divide 20 by 2
4. Divide 21 by 2
5. Half of 15

Create a number chain. The children stand in a line or circle. The first child halves the starting number, the next child halves it again, and so on. The child who says a fraction sits down and is 'out' of the game, which continues with a new starting number.

6. 16
7. 24
8. 20
9. 36
10. 52
11. 86
12. 60
13. 32
14. 78
15. 38

Answers

1. 8
2. 8½
3. 10
4. 10½
5. 7½
6. 8, 4, 2, 1, ½
7. 12, 6, 3, 1½
8. 10, 5, 2½
9. 18, 9, 4½
10. 26, 13, 6½
11. 43, 21½
12. 30, 15, 7½
13. 16, 8, 4, 2, 1, ½
14. 39, 19½
15. 19, 9½

85 Shading shapes

Resources
Squared paper

Learning objective
Find fractions of numbers, quantities or shapes (e.g. $^1/_5$ of 30 plums, $^3/_8$ of a 6 by 4 rectangle)

Type of starter
Refresh

Mental strategy
Counting or calculating the number of small squares in shapes to help calculate how many squares to shade

Clarifying strategies for working out equivalent fractions

Answers
1. 12 small squares shaded out of 24, $^1/_2$
2. 3 small squares shaded out of 9, $^2/_3$
3. 4 small squares shaded out of 16, $^{12}/_{16}$ or $^3/_4$
4. 10 small squares shaded out of 25, $^{15}/_{25}$ or $^3/_5$
5. 3 small squares shaded out of 8, $^5/_8$

Ask the children to follow these instructions and answer the questions.

1. Draw a 6 × 4 rectangle. Shade $^1/_2$.
   What fraction of the 6 × 4 rectangle is not shaded?
2. Draw a 3 × 3 square. Shade $^1/_3$.
   What fraction of the 3 × 3 square is not shaded?
3. Draw an 8 × 2 rectangle. Shade $^1/_4$.
   How many sixteenths are not shaded? Write your answer in sixteenths and then as an equivalent fraction in quarters.
4. Draw a 5 × 5 square. Shade $^2/_5$.
   How many small squares are not shaded? What is this as a fraction of the whole square?
5. Draw a 4 × 2 rectangle. Shade $^3/_8$.
   What fraction is not shaded?

86 Which operation?

Learning objective
Choose and carry out appropriate calculations, using calculator methods where appropriate

Type of starter
Reason

Mental strategy
Remembering that subtraction is the inverse of addition, and that division is the inverse of multiplication

Remembering that when doing an inverse operation the digits themselves do not change, just the order

Resources
Calculator (optional, at teacher's discretion)

Read out the following questions. Children should identify the missing number operation in each question, then write the calculation that is the inverse operation.

1.	6 ? 4 = 24	5.	11 ? 7 = 18	9.	100 ? 10 = 10
2.	27 ? 3 = 9	6.	32 ? 4 = 8	10.	60 ? 43 = 17
3.	15 ? 6 = 9	7.	64 ? 4 =16	11.	5 ? 20 = 100
4.	9 ? 5 = 45	8.	16 ? 16 = 32	12.	3 ? 15 = 45

Answers
1. × 24 ÷ 4 = 6
2. ÷ 9 × 3 = 27
3. − 9 + 6 = 15
4. × 45 ÷ 5 = 9
5. + 18 − 7 = 11
6. ÷ 8 × 4 = 32
7. ÷ 16 × 4 = 64
8. + 32 − 16 = 16
9. ÷ 10 × 10 = 100
10. − 17 + 43 = 60
11. × 100 ÷ 20 = 5
12. × 45 ÷ 15 = 3

87 Multiplication clock

Learning objective
Derive and recall multiplication facts up to 10 × 10, the corresponding division facts and multiples of numbers to 10 up to the tenth multiple

Type of starter
Recall

Resources
Pointer; on the board: clock face

Point to each number round the clock in turn, as children chant each number fact twice (for example: 2 × 1 = 1 (twice), 2 × 7 = 14 (twice), and so on).

Now point to the numbers at random, asking for a rapid answer each time.

Repeat for the 4-times table, concentrating on the less well-known facts.

No set answers

88 Tables bingo (6, 7, 8, 9)

Resources
Paper and a pencil for each child

Learning objective
Derive and recall multiplication facts up to 10 × 10, the corresponding division facts and multiples of numbers to 10 up to the tenth multiple

Type of starter
Recall

Ask the children to choose eight multiples of 6, 7, 8 and/or 9 and write them spread out on their paper.

Read out the questions. If the children have the answer to a question on their paper, they cross it out. The first child to cross out all eight numbers wins.

Repeat, using the questions in a different order.

1.	5 × 6	16.	6 × 3
2.	2 × 7	17.	7 × 9
3.	10 × 8	18.	3 × 9
4.	5 × 9	19.	1 × 8
5.	3 × 8	20.	10 × 6
6.	3 × 3	21.	7 × 7
7.	4 × 8	22.	2 × 6
8.	8 × 8	23.	9 × 9
9.	10 × 7	24.	5 × 7
10.	1 × 6	25.	4 × 10
11.	8 × 6	26.	1 × 7
12.	2 × 8	27.	7 × 6
13.	4 × 7	28.	3 × 7
14.	10 × 9	29.	6 × 6
15.	8 × 7	30.	8 × 9

Answers

1. 30
2. 14
3. 80
4. 45
5. 24
6. 9
7. 32
8. 64
9. 70
10. 6
11. 48
12. 16
13. 28
14. 90
15. 56
16. 18
17. 63
18. 27
19. 8
20. 60
21. 49
22. 12
23. 81
24. 35
25. 40
26. 7
27. 42
28. 21
29. 36
30. 72

89 Mixed numbers

Learning objective
Use diagrams to identify equivalent fractions (e.g. $^{6}/_{8}$ and $^{3}/_{4}$, or $^{70}/_{100}$ and $^{7}/_{10}$); interpret mixed numbers and position them on a number line (e.g. $3^{1}/_{2}$)

Type of starter
Rehearse

Resources
0–10 number lines marked in quarters and tenths (from photocopiable page 92)

Answers
See answers below right

Ask the children to position the following mixed numbers on their number lines:

1. 2½
2. 3¼
3. 5¾
4. 1½
5. 4½
6. 6¼
7. 8¾
8. $4^{7}/_{10}$
9. $3^{1}/_{10}$
10. $2^{4}/_{10}$
11. $1^{1}/_{10}$
12. $5^{9}/_{10}$

Answers

1–7

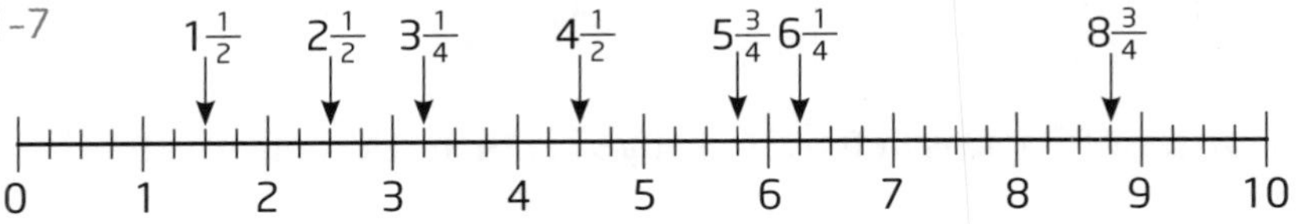

8–12

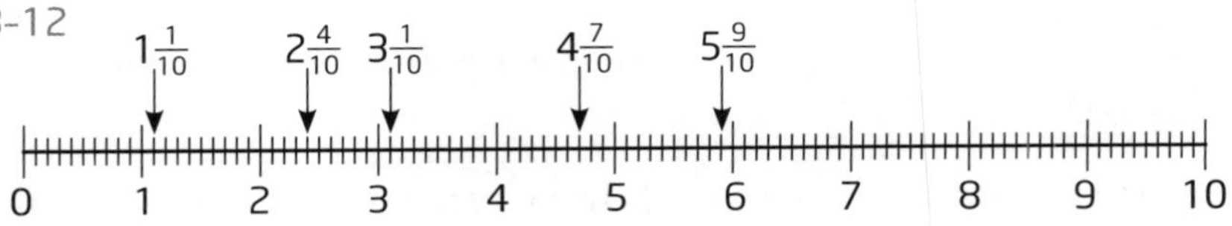

90 Half number chains

Learning objective
Find fractions of numbers, quantities or shapes (e.g. $^{1}/_{5}$ of 30 plums, $^{3}/_{8}$ of a 6 by 4 rectangle)

Type of starter
Recall

Resources
Board or flipchart

The children stand in a line. The first child halves the start number, which is halved again by the second child, and so on. The child who says a fraction is 'out' of the game and sits down.

1. 88
2. 72
3. 96
4. 68
5. 64
6. 92
7. 56
8. 76
9. 84
10. 80

Answers

1. 44, 22, 11, 5½
2. 36, 18, 9, 4½
3. 48, 24, 12, 6, 3, 1½
4. 34, 17, 8½
5. 32, 16, 8, 4, 2, 1, ½
6. 46, 23, 11½
7. 28, 14, 7, 3½
8. 38, 19, 9½
9. 42, 21, 10½
10. 40, 20, 10, 5, 2½

91 What's my value?

Resources
None

Learning objective
Find fractions of numbers, quantities or shapes (e.g. $^1/_5$ of 30 plums, $^3/_8$ of a 6 by 4 rectangle)

Type of starter
Refresh

Mental strategy
Revision of litre-ml, km-m and kg-g equivalents

Using division to find unit fractions

Using multiplication to find multiples of the unit fraction

Ask the children to use their knowledge of fractions to solve the following problems.

1. A jug of water holds 1 litre and it is shared equally between four people. How much water does each person get in their glass?
2. There are 16 apples in the box. I buy ¾ of them. How many is that?
3. I ran 2km, which was five laps. How many metres was each lap?
4. £10 was shared equally amongst four children. How much did each one get?
5. A box of chocolates contained 50 chocolates. It was divided into two layers. How many were in each layer?
6. A large cake weighed 2kg. It was cut into ten equal slices. What did each slice weigh? Answer in grams.
7. There are 24 coloured pencils in a tub. $^1/_8$ of them are shades of red. How many red coloured pencils are there?
8. $^2/_5$ of the class are girls. How many girls are there in the class of 30?
9. How many boys are there in the same class?
10. ¼ of the girls in the same class are called Jessica. How many girls are called Jessica?

Answers

1. 250ml
2. 12
3. 400m
4. £2.50
5. 25
6. 200g
7. Three
8. 12
9. 18
10. Three

92 Match the equal values (1)

Learning objective
Recognise the equivalence between decimal and fraction forms of one half, quarters, tenths and hundredths

Type of starter
Rehearse

Mental strategy
Recognising decimals and finding equivalent fractions

Resources
Paper for each child; glue; one fraction and decimal grid per child (see activity)

$^{1}/_{10}$	0.4	0.1	$^{50}/_{100}$	$^{8}/_{10}$
0.3	0.5	0.6	$^{7}/_{10}$	$^{90}/_{100}$
$^{2}/_{10}$	$^{60}/_{100}$	$^{40}/_{100}$	0.8	$^{70}/_{100}$
$^{3}/_{10}$	$^{5}/_{10}$	0.9	0.7	
$^{9}/_{10}$	$^{6}/_{10}$	$^{20}/_{100}$	$^{80}/_{100}$	
0.2	$^{10}/_{100}$	$^{30}/_{100}$	$^{4}/_{10}$	

Make enlarged photocopies of the above grid and give a copy to each child. Ask the children to cut out the decimals and fractions along the grid lines. They should then identify the decimals and arrange them in a column, before finding their fraction equivalents and placing them in the correct row. Match the equivalents by placing them in a row. When the children have finished this, they can glue the numbers onto a separate piece of paper.

Answers

0.1, $^{1}/_{10}$, $^{10}/_{100}$
0.2, $^{2}/_{10}$, $^{20}/_{100}$
0.3, $^{3}/_{10}$, $^{30}/_{100}$
0.4, $^{4}/_{10}$, $^{40}/_{100}$
0.5, $^{5}/_{10}$, $^{50}/_{100}$
0.6, $^{6}/_{10}$, $^{60}/_{100}$
0.7, $^{7}/_{10}$, $^{70}/_{100}$
0.8, $^{8}/_{10}$, $^{80}/_{100}$
0.9, $^{9}/_{10}$, $^{90}/_{100}$

93 Match the pairs

Learning objective
Identify pairs of fractions that total 1

Type of starter
Reason

Mental strategy
Checking denominators are the same and that numerators total 1

Resources
Paper for each child; glue; one fraction grid per child (see activity)

One fifth	One half	Eight tenths	Four fifths	Three sixteenths
Two tenths	Two thirds	Seven eighths	One half	Seven sixteenths
One quarter	Three tenths	Three quarters	One third	Nine sixteenths
Seven tenths	One eighth	One sixth	Five sixths	Thirteen sixteenths

Ask the children to cut out the fractions along the grid lines. They should then write the numeral equivalent on the back of each fraction, before pairing up the fractions that total 1. When they have finished, they can glue the numbers onto a separate piece of paper.

Answers

$^{1}/_{2} + ^{1}/_{2}$
$^{1}/_{3} + ^{2}/_{3}$
$^{2}/_{10} + ^{8}/_{10}$
$^{1}/_{5} + ^{4}/_{5}$
$^{3}/_{16} + ^{13}/_{16}$
$^{7}/_{10} + ^{3}/_{10}$
$^{1}/_{8} + ^{7}/_{8}$
$^{1}/_{6} + ^{5}/_{6}$
$^{1}/_{4} + ^{3}/_{4}$
$^{7}/_{16} + ^{9}/_{16}$

94 Division snap

Resources
Four of five sets of 1-9 numeral cards (from photocopiable page 89)

Learning objective
Derive and recall multiplication facts up to 10 × 10, the corresponding division facts and multiples of numbers to 10 up to the tenth multiple

Type of starter
Recall

Answers

1. 2
2. 5
3. 8
4. 3
5. 7
6. 1
7. 9
8. 6
9. 4
10. 6
11. 3
12. 5
13. 1
14. 9
15. 4

Deal about four number cards to each child. Read out a question. Those children who have the answer on a card hold up the card and say 'Snap'.

1. 10 ÷ 5
2. 50 ÷ 10
3. 24 ÷ 3
4. 6 ÷ 2
5. 28 ÷ 4
6. 5 ÷ 5
7. 18 ÷ 2
8. 24 ÷ 4
9. 40 ÷ 10
10. 12 ÷ 2
11. 9 ÷ 3
12. 20 ÷ 4
13. 10 ÷ 10
14. 45 ÷ 5
15. 16 ÷ 4

95 Match the equal values (2)

Resources
Paper for each child; glue; one fraction and decimal grid per child (see activity)

Learning objective
Recognise the equivalence between decimal and fraction forms of one half, quarters, tenths and hundredths

Type of starter
Recall

Mental strategy
Recognising decimals and finding equivalent fractions

Answers

0.25, $^{1}/_{4}$, $^{25}/_{100}$
0.5, $^{1}/_{2}$, $^{5}/_{10}$
0.75, $^{3}/_{4}$, $^{75}/_{100}$
1.5, $1^{1}/_{2}$
0.7, $^{7}/_{10}$, $^{70}/_{100}$
2.25, $2^{1}/_{4}$
3.75, $3^{3}/_{4}$

0.75	0.25	3.75	$^{1}/_{2}$	$^{1}/_{4}$
$^{70}/_{100}$	$^{3}/_{4}$	$^{25}/_{100}$	$^{75}/_{100}$	$1^{1}/_{2}$
1.5	$^{7}/_{10}$	0.7	0.5	$2^{1}/_{4}$
2.25	$3^{3}/_{4}$	$^{5}/_{10}$		

Make enlarged photocopies of the above grid and give a copy to each child. Ask the children to cut out the decimals and fractions along the grid lines. They should then identify the decimals and arrange them in a column, before finding their fraction equivalents and placing them in the correct row. Match the equivalents by placing them in a row. When they have finished, they can glue the numbers onto a separate piece of paper.

96 Fractions of shapes

Learning objective
Find fractions of numbers, quantities or shapes (e.g. $^1/_5$ of 30 plums, $^3/_8$ of a 6 by 4 rectangle)

Type of starter
Refresh

Mental strategy
Using the denominator to divide the number of squares (for example: 24 ÷ 2 = 12 to find ½ of 24)

Using the denominator to find a unit fraction, them multiplying by the numerator (for example: $^2/_3$ of 9 is (9 ÷ 3) × 2 = 6)

Resources
On the board: illustration of a 6 × 4 rectangle

Show the children the 6 × 4 rectangle. Explain that it has an area of 6 × 4 = 24 squares. Ask: *How many squares make:*

1. ½ of the rectangle?
2. ¼ of the rectangle?
3. ¾ of the rectangle?
4. $^1/_3$ of the rectangle?
5. $^2/_3$ of the rectangle?
6. $^1/_8$ of the rectangle?
7. $^3/_8$ of the rectangle?
8. $^5/_8$ of the rectangle?

Ask:

9. How many squares would ½ of a 6 × 2 rectangle be?
10. How many squares would ¼ of a 6 × 2 rectangle be?
11. How many squares would $^1/_3$ of a 6 × 2 rectangle be?
12. How many squares would $^2/_3$ of a 6 × 2 rectangle be?
13. How many squares would ¼ of a 4 × 4 square be?
14. How many squares would ¾ of a 4 × 4 square be?
15. How many squares would $^1/_8$ of a 4 × 4 square be?
16. How many squares would $^1/_{16}$ of a 4 × 4 square be?

Answers
1. 12
2. 6
3. 18
4. 8
5. 16
6. 3
7. 9
8. 15
9. 6
10. 3
11. 4
12. 8
13. 4
14. 12
15. 2
16. 1

97 More fractions

Resources
One blank 100-square for each pair (from photocopiable page 95); two different-coloured pencils for each pair

Learning objective
Recognise the equivalence between decimal and fraction forms of one half, quarters, tenths and hundredths

Type of starter
Rehearse

Mental strategy
Recalling decimal equivalents of half, quarters, tenths and hundredths

Answers

1. ½ , $^{5}/_{10}$, $^{50}/_{100}$, 0.5
2. $^{10}/_{100}$, 0.1
3. $^{20}/_{100}$, 0.2
4. $^{25}/_{100}$, 0.25
5. $^{75}/_{100}$, 0.75

Ask each pair of children to label all the squares on their 100-square in hundredths ($^{1}/_{100}$, $^{2}/_{100}$, $^{3}/_{100}$ ... $^{100}/_{100}$). They should take turns doing alternate rows (of 10), using a different-coloured pencil each. Then ask:

1. What fraction of the total number of squares has each of you labelled? Write this fraction in three different ways. What is this as a decimal?
2. How many 100ths are there in one row? What is this as a decimal?
3. How many 100ths are there in two rows? What is this as a decimal?
4. How many 100ths are there in ¼ of the square? What is this as a decimal?
5. How many 100ths are there in ¾ of the square? What is this as a decimal?

98 Counting in quarters

Resources
0-3 number line with quarters marked (from photocopiable page 92) for each child

Learning objective
Use diagrams to identify equivalent fractions (e.g. $^{6}/_{8}$ and $^{3}/_{4}$, or $^{70}/_{100}$ and $^{7}/_{10}$); interpret mixed numbers and position them on a number line (e.g. $3^{1}/_{2}$)

Type of starter
Rehearse

Mental strategy
Counting on and counting back in ones on a regular number line

Applying the same strategy counting on and back in quarters

Answers

1. ¾
2. 1¼
3. 1
4. 1½
5. 1
6. ¼
7. 2½
8. 2

Ask the children to help you count in quarters from zero up to 3: 0, ¼, ½, ¾ ... 3.

Give the children a blank number line. Ask them to mark all the quarters from 0 to 3.

Now ask them to use their number line as instructed. After each question, ask: *What is the answer?*

Count up $^{2}/_{4}$ from:	1.	¼	2.	¾
Count up ¾ from:	3.	¼	4.	¾
Count back ¾ from:	5.	1¾	6.	1
Count back ¼ from:	7.	2¾	8.	2¼

99 Fraction search

Learning objective
Find fractions of numbers, quantities or shapes (e.g. $^1/_5$ of 30 plums, $^3/_8$ of a 6 by 4 rectangle)

Type of starter
Refresh

Mental strategy
Remembering to divide by the denominator and multiply by the numerator

Resources
Paper and pencil for each child

Challenge the children to see how quickly they can answer these questions.

1. $^1/_4$ of £50
2. $^1/_2$ of £23
3. $^1/_3$ of £18.99
4. $^2/_3$ of £21
5. $^3/_4$ of £30
6. $^1/_8$ of 80cm
7. $^5/_8$ of 80m
8. $^1/_6$ of 36 eggs
9. $^9/_{10}$ of 100 pencils
10. $^1/_{10}$ of £1.50

Tell the children that in questions 11–20 the larger amount is the denominator and the smaller amount is the numerator; they need to ensure both quantities are expressed in the same terms.

11. What fraction of 10 metres is 5 metres?
12. What fraction of £1.00 is 75p?
13. What fraction of 1 litre is 200ml?
14. What fraction of 5 litres is 4 litres?
15. What fraction of 1kg is 600g?

Answers

1. £12.50
2. £11.50
3. £6.33
4. £14
5. £22.50
6. 10cm
7. 50m
8. 6 eggs
9. 90 pencils
10. 15p
11. $^1/_2$
12. $^3/_4$
13. $^1/_5$
14. $^4/_5$
15. $^6/_{10}$ or $^3/_5$

100 Problems of proportion (1)

Resources
Pencil and paper for each child

Learning objective
Use the vocabulary of ratio and proportion to describe the relationship between two quantities; estimate a proportion

Type of starter
Reason

Mental strategy
Relating the vocabulary of ratio and proportion to a fraction

Answers

1. 12
2. 6 red, 9 green
3. 9
4. £6
5. 4

Ask the children to answer the following questions.

1. On a string of beads there are 30 beads. There are two orange beads to every three yellow beads. How many beads are orange?
2. In a box of toys there are two red cars to every three green cars. There are 15 cars in the box. How many are there of each colour?
3. In a basket of fruit there are apples, pears and bananas. They are in equal proportion. There are 27 pieces of fruit. How many of each fruit are there?
4. For every £1 pocket money my mum gives me, I get 50p from my Gran. How much has Gran given me when my mum has given me £12?
5. On the pond there are six geese to every two swans. Complete this statement: one in every ... birds are swans.

101 Problems of proportion (2)

Resources
One bag containing 40 cubes (8 red, 16 green, 4 yellow, 12 blue) for each group of four children

Learning objective
Use the vocabulary of ratio and proportion to describe the relationship between two quantities; estimate a proportion

Type of starter
Refine

Mental strategy
Finding a proportion as a fraction and reducing it to its lowest terms

Answers

$^{40}/_{40}$ = 1 whole bag

2 cubes in every 10 are red ($^{8}/_{40} = ^{1}/_{5}$ red)

4 cubes in every 10 are green ($^{16}/_{40} = ^{2}/_{5}$ green)

1 cube in every 10 is yellow ($^{4}/_{40} = ^{1}/_{10}$ yellow)

3 cubes in every 10 is blue ($^{12}/_{40} = ^{3}/_{10}$ blue)

Ask each group of four children to take the cubes out of the bag and to take one colour each.

Ask the children to work together to write statements about the contents of their bag, using the vocabulary of ratio and proportion. Each group should appoint a scribe. After five minutes, invite groups to read out their statements and discuss whether they are correct.

If there is time, ask the children to express their findings as fractions as well.

Shape snap cards

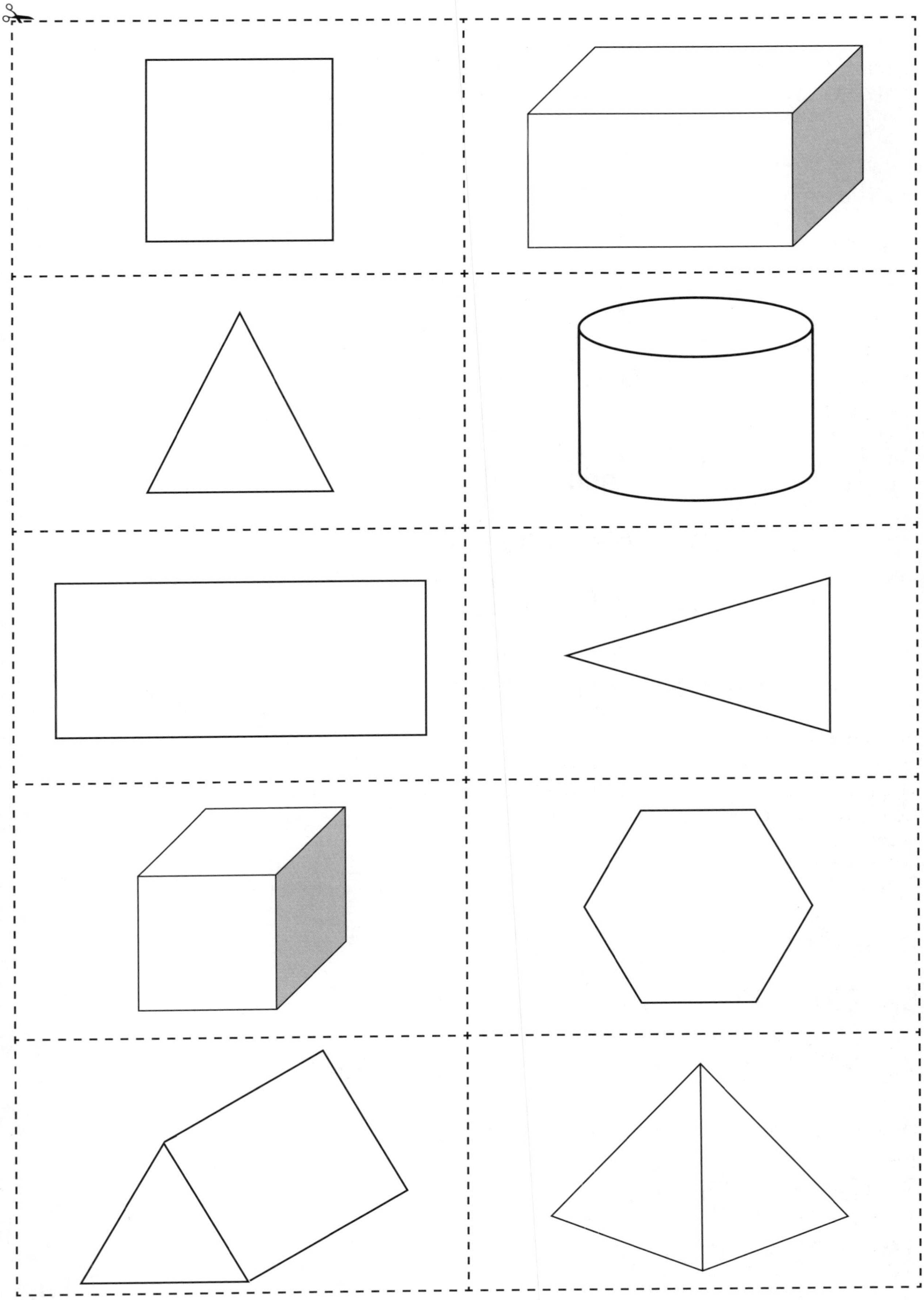

Odds and evens addition grid

+	1	2	3	4
1				
2				
3				
4				

odd + odd = ___________

even + even = ___________

odd + even = ___________

1. 14 + 11 = even + odd = odd
2. 26 + 12 = ___________ + ___________ = ___________
3. 17 + 18 = ___________ + ___________ = ___________
4. 232 + 214 = ___________ + ___________ = ___________
5. 380 + 146 = ___________ + ___________ = ___________
6. 291 + 603 = ___________ + ___________ = ___________
7. 449 + 256 = ___________ + ___________ = ___________
8. 1728 + 1173 = ___________ + ___________ = ___________
9. 2062 + 3150 = ___________ + ___________ = ___________
10. 4295 + 1389 = ___________ + ___________ = ___________

0–9 numeral cards

0	1
2	3
4	5
6	7
8	9

Tables snap cards

12	14	16	18
21	24	27	28
32	36	20	25
30	35	40	45

Number lines (1)

Decimal number lines

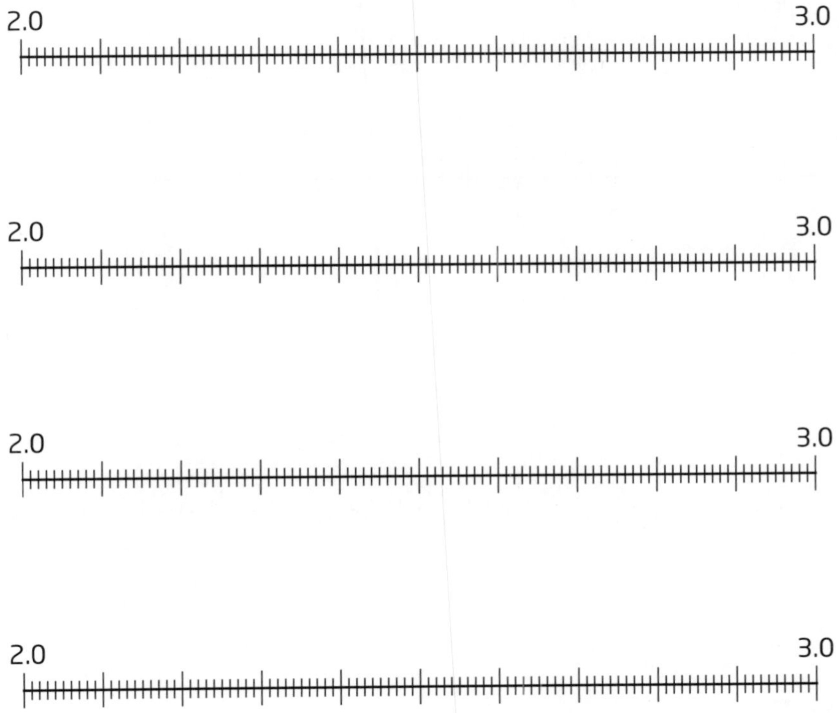

Number lines

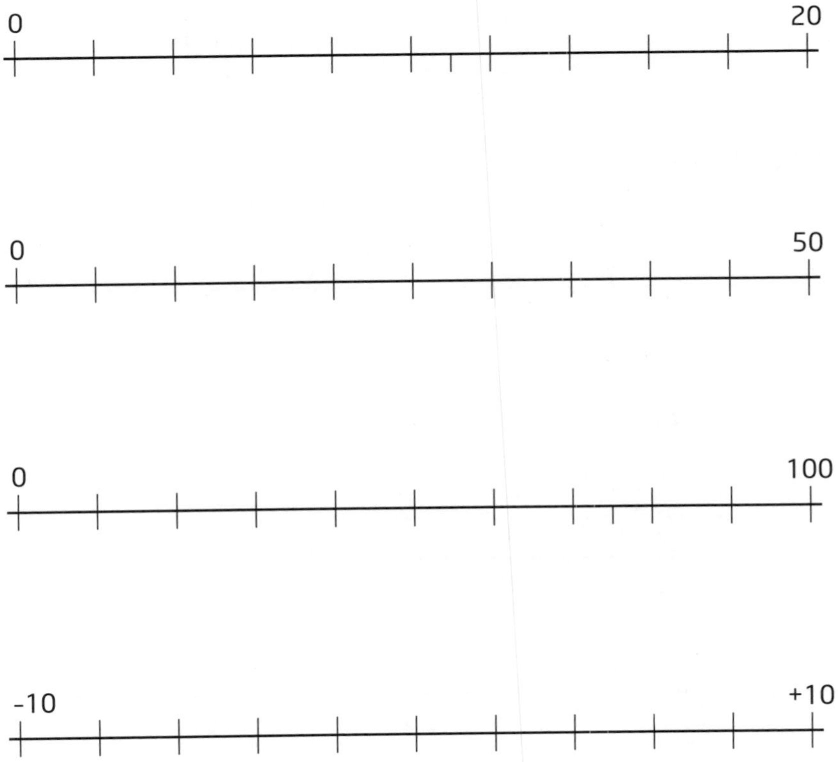

Number lines (2)

0-10 number lines

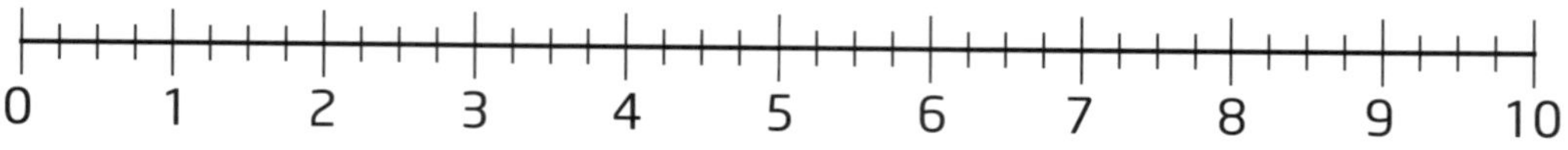

0-3 number line

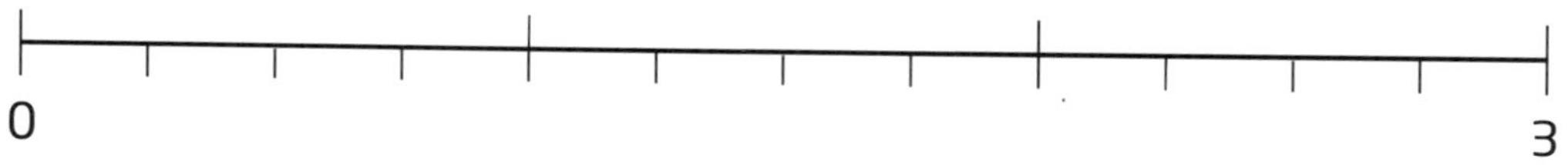

Blank number lines

2D shapes

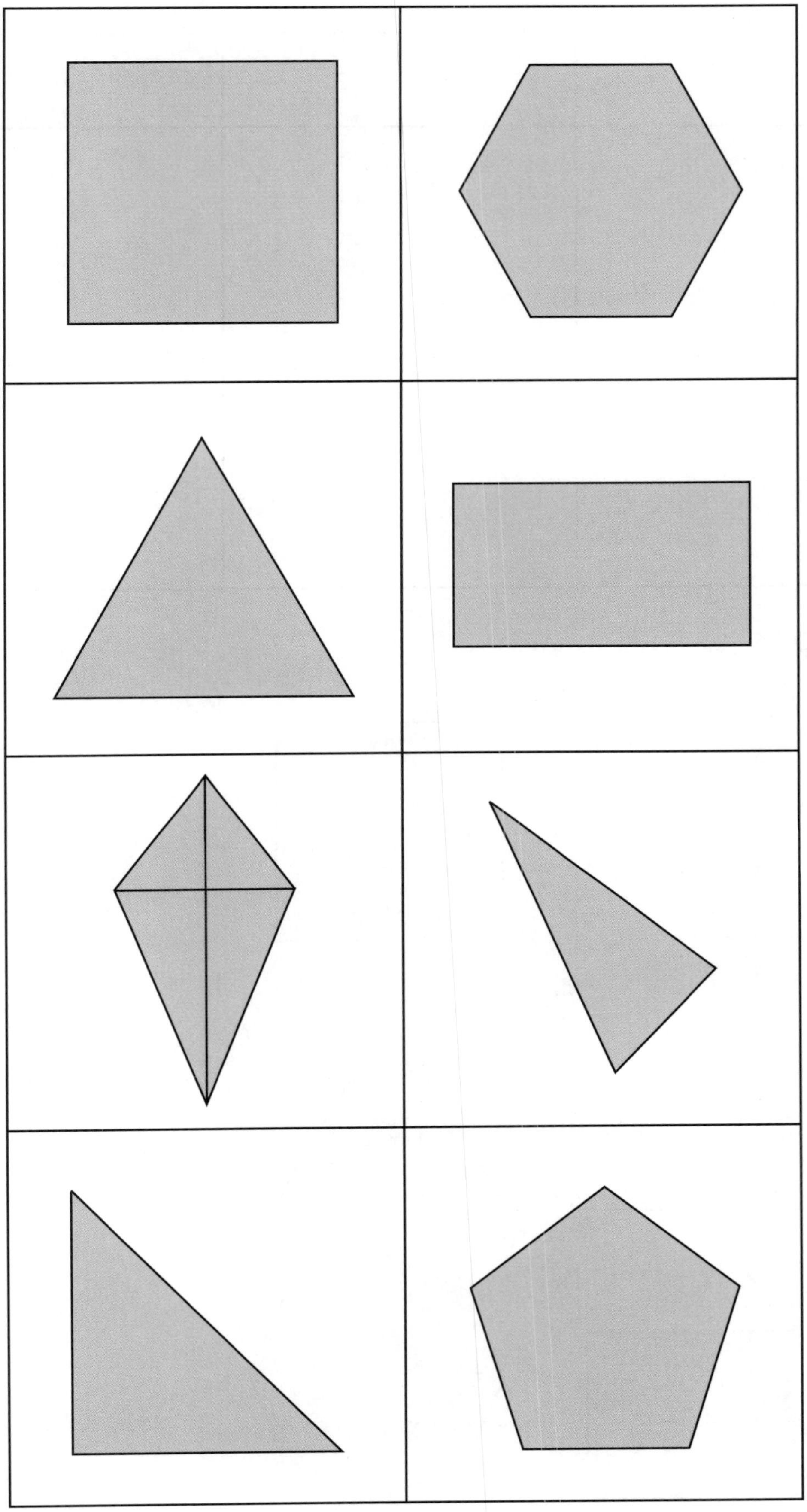

Carroll diagram and 2D shapes

Carroll diagram

2D shapes

a.

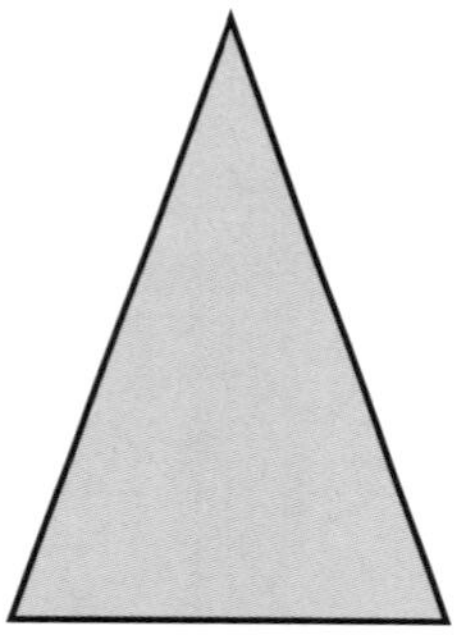

b.

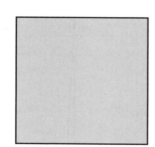

c.

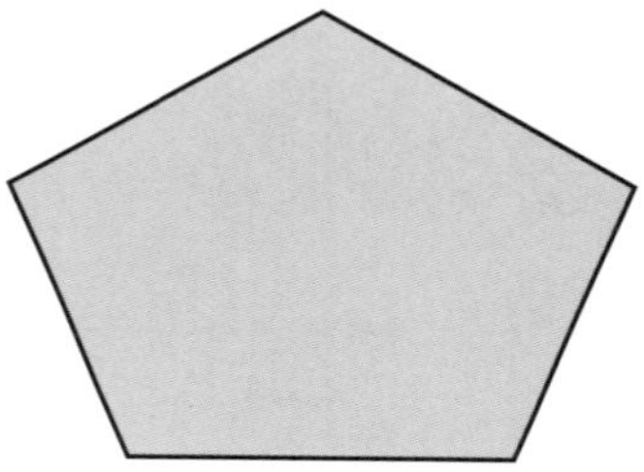

d.

e.

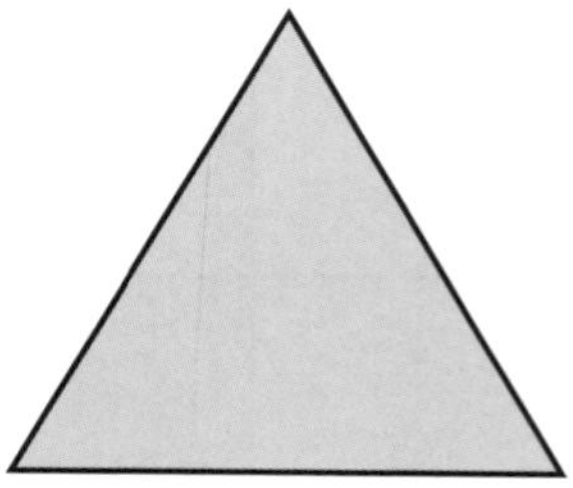

f.

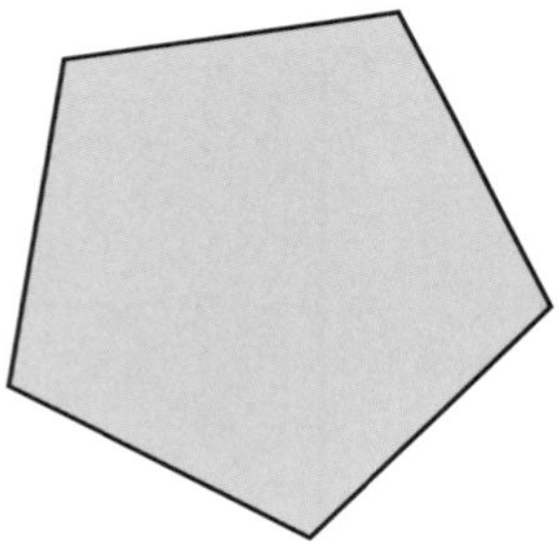

g.

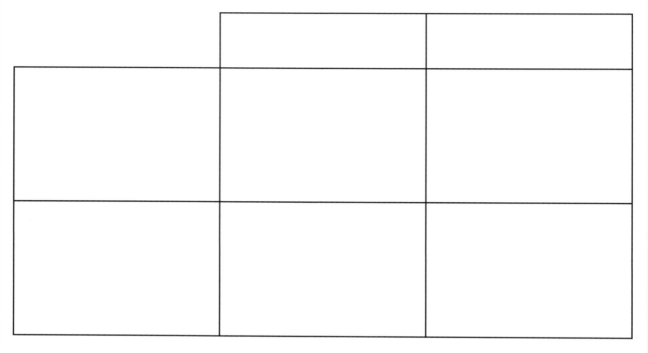

h.

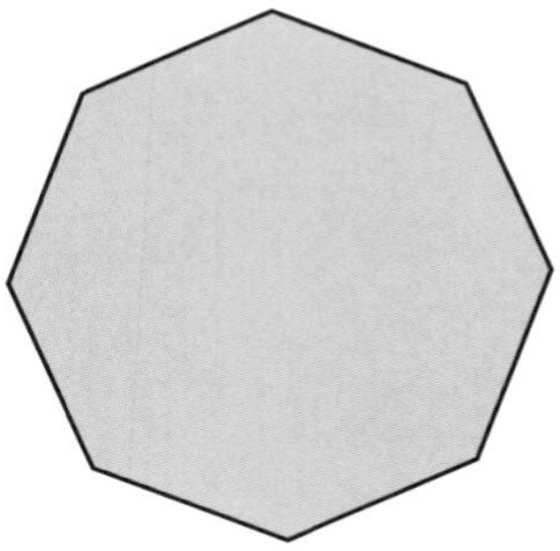

100-square

Level 3: Oral and mental assessments

Teachers' notes

Time: 20 minutes for each complete paper.

- Children should sit so that they cannot see each other's work.
- Do not explain questions or read numbers to the children.
- The test may be administered to groups of children or to the whole class.
- There are 20 marks available for each paper.
- Less confident learners could give their answers orally to a teaching assistant or other adult who could record their answers.

Delivering the tests

- Read each question to the children twice.
- Allow five seconds for each of the first 15 questions and ten seconds for each of the last five questions.
- Answers to be recorded on the answer sheets provided.
- One mark per question: 20 marks total.

Say to the children:

'I am going to read some questions for you to answer. I will read each question twice. You will have five seconds to answer some questions and 10 seconds to answer some questions at the end of the test.'

'For most of the questions you will write your answer in a box.' [Show example.]

'For some questions you may need to tick the right answer.'

'If you make a mistake, you should cross it out and write your answer again clearly.'

Levelling the children

Add up the marks.
(Possible total: 20 marks)

Below Level 3	0 - 7 marks
Low Level 3	8 - 12 marks
Secure Level 3	13 - 15 marks
High Level 3	16 - 20 marks

This assessment reflects a child's performance in mental maths. When awarding an end-of-year teacher assessment level, teachers also need to consider a child's performance on periodic and day-to-day assessments over all learning objectives.

Test 1: Mental maths assessment

Oral and mental questions (page 1 of 2)

Time: 20 minutes

- Read each question twice to the children.
- Answers to be recorded on the answer sheet on pages 99-100.
- One mark per question: 20 marks total.
- Allow five seconds for each answer for questions 1-15; allow ten seconds for questions 16-20.

	Question	Answer
1	Write the number six thousand and forty-two.	6042
2	Calculate 65 + 21.	86
3	I have £1.00. I spend 76p. How much do I have left?	24p
4	*(Look at the fractions.)* Tick the fraction that is the same as $^6/_8$.	$^3/_4$
5	I have 246p. What is that in pounds and pence?	£2.46
6	I am thinking of a number. I double it and then add 10. My answer is 26. What was my number?	8
7	What do we call angles that are less than 90°?	acute
8	What is 8 × 3?	24
9	*(Look at the net.)* Tick the 3D shape that this net will make.	cuboid
10	How many centimetres are there in 4.5 metres?	450cm
11	*(Look at the clock.)* What time is it?	11.05 or five past 11
12	I am thinking of a number between 30 and 39. It is a multiple of 4 and also a multiple of 6. What number could it be?	36

Test 1: Mental maths assessment

Oral and mental questions (page 2 of 2)

	Question	Answer
13	*(Look at the coins.)* How much money is there?	£3.73
14	Amy is 163 centimetres tall. What is that to the nearest 10 centimetres?	160cm
15	What is the perimeter of an equilateral triangle if one side is 9cm long?	27cm
16	A square tile has an area of 100 square centimetres. What is the length of one of its sides?	10cm
17	If I practise reading for 15 minutes every night for a week, how long will I have spent reading?	1¾ hours, 1 hour 45 minutes or 105 minutes
18	*(Look at the Carroll diagram.)* Look at the shapes of the numerals in the diagram. Tick the number that is in the wrong place.	7
19	There are 32 counters. Half of them are blue and a quarter of them are red. The rest are green. How many are green?	8
20	The temperature during the day is 14°C. At night it is 20° colder. What is the night-time temperature?	-6°C

End of test

Name Date

Test 1: Mental maths assessment

Oral and mental assessment answer sheet (1 of 2)

	Answer			Mark
1				
2				
3				
4	$\frac{2}{3}$	$\frac{3}{4}$	$\frac{2}{5}$	
5				
6				
7				
8				
9	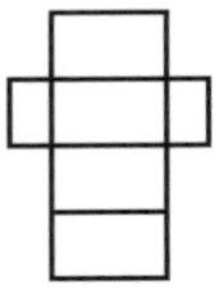 cube ☐	cuboid ☐	rectangle ☐	
10				
11	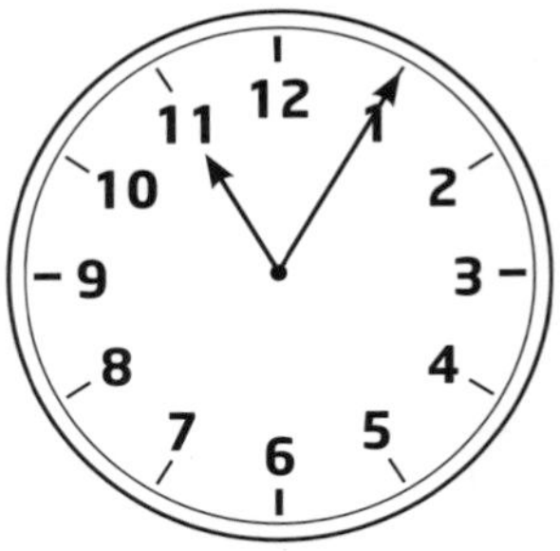			

Name Date

Test 1: Mental maths assessment

Oral and mental assessment answer sheet (2 of 2)

<table>
<tr><th></th><th>Answer</th><th>Mark</th></tr>
<tr><td>12</td><td></td><td></td></tr>
<tr><td>13</td><td></td><td></td></tr>
<tr><td>14</td><td></td><td></td></tr>
<tr><td>15</td><td></td><td></td></tr>
<tr><td>16</td><td></td><td></td></tr>
<tr><td>17</td><td></td><td></td></tr>
<tr><td>18</td><td><table><tr><th></th><th>Straight lines</th><th>No straight lines</th></tr><tr><td>Curved lines</td><td>5</td><td>3</td></tr><tr><td>No curved lines</td><td>4</td><td>7</td></tr></table></td><td></td></tr>
<tr><td>19</td><td></td><td></td></tr>
<tr><td>20</td><td></td><td></td></tr>
</table>

End of test

Total	

Test 2: Mental maths assessment

Oral and mental questions (page 1 of 2)

Time: 20 minutes

- Read each question twice to the children.
- Answers to be recorded on the answer sheet on pages 103-104.
- One mark per question: 20 marks total.
- Allow five seconds for each answer for questions 1-15; allow ten seconds for questions 16-20.

	Question	Answer
1	What number is one hundred more than 674?	774
2	What is the difference between 52 and 47?	5
3	A packet of crisps costs 40p. How many can I buy for £2.40?	6
4	*(Look at the shape.)* Tick the correct name.	octagon
5	How many months are there in a year?	12
6	Carrots are 64p per kilogram. How much is half a kilogram?	32p
7	What is 9 × 4?	36
8	*(Look at the shape.)* How many faces does the shape have?	6
9	Sam weighs 32 kilograms. How many grams is that?	32,000 grams
10	We start school at 9.05 and go for assembly at 9.55. How long is the first lesson?	50 minutes
11	I am facing south and turn anti-clockwise 90 degrees. Tick the direction I am now facing.	east
12	*(Look at the shape.)* Tick the correct name.	equilateral triangle

Test 2: Mental maths assessment

Oral and mental questions (page 2 of 2)

	Question	Answer
13	*(Look at the decimals.)* Tick the greatest number.	1.6
14	A multiple of 3 must be an odd number. True or false? Tick the right answer.	false
15	Each side of a regular pentagon measures eight centimetres. What is the total length of all its sides?	40cm
16	There are 27 children in my class. One third of them are girls. How many are boys?	18
17	*(Look at the table.)* How many fewer children liked plain than spring onion crisps?	13
18	Tom has 1 litre of water. He pours out 350 millilitres. How much water is left?	650ml
19	I am thinking of a multiple of 5. I double it and add 4. My answer is 64. What was my number?	30
20	Five apples cost 67p. How much does each apple cost to the nearest penny?	13p

End of test

Name Date

Test 2: Mental maths assessment

Oral and mental assessment answer sheet (page 1 of 2)

	Answer	Mark
1		
2		
3		
4	 octagon ☐ hexagon ☐ pentagon ☐	
5		
6		
7		
8	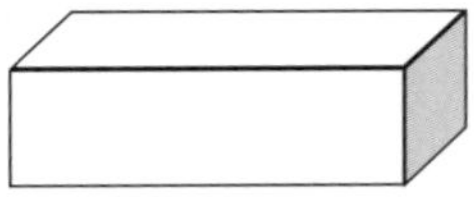	
9		
10		
11	 north ☐ south ☐ east ☐ west ☐	

Name Date

Test 2: Mental maths assessment

Oral and mental assessment answer sheet (page 2 of 2)

<table>
<tr><th></th><th>Answer</th><th>Mark</th></tr>
<tr><td>12</td><td> right-angled triangle ☐ equilateral triangle ☐</td><td></td></tr>
<tr><td>13</td><td>1.06 ☐ 1.6 ☐ 1.16 ☐</td><td></td></tr>
<tr><td>14</td><td>true ☐ false ☐</td><td></td></tr>
<tr><td>15</td><td></td><td></td></tr>
<tr><td>16</td><td></td><td></td></tr>
<tr><td>17</td><td><table>
<tr><th>Type of crisps</th><th>Number of children</th></tr>
<tr><td>Plain</td><td>15</td></tr>
<tr><td>Salt and vinegar</td><td>19</td></tr>
<tr><td>Spring onion</td><td>28</td></tr>
<tr><td>Smokey bacon</td><td>13</td></tr>
<tr><td>Sweet chilli</td><td>5</td></tr>
</table></td><td></td></tr>
<tr><td>18</td><td></td><td></td></tr>
<tr><td>19</td><td></td><td></td></tr>
<tr><td>20</td><td></td><td></td></tr>
</table>

End of test

Total	

Level 4: Oral and mental assessments

Teachers' notes

Time: 20 minutes for each complete paper.

- Children should sit so that they cannot see each other's work.
- Do not explain questions or read numbers to the children.
- The test may be administered to groups of children or to the whole class.
- There are 20 marks available for each paper.

Delivering the tests
- Read each question to the children twice.
- Allow five seconds each for questions 1-5, ten seconds for questions 6-15, and fifteen seconds for questions 16-20.
- Answers to be recorded on the answer sheets provided.

Say to the children:

'I am going to read some questions for you to answer. I will read each question twice. You will have five seconds to answer the first five questions, then ten seconds to answer the next ten questions and finally 15 seconds for the last five questions.'

'For most of the questions you will write your answer in a box.' [Show example.]

'For some questions you may need to tick the right answer.'

'If you make a mistake, you should cross it out and write your answer again clearly.'

Levelling the children
Add up the marks.
(Possible total: 20 marks)

Below Level 4	0 - 7 marks
Low Level 4	8 - 12 marks
Secure Level 4	13 - 15 marks
High Level 4	16 - 20 marks

This assessment reflects a child's performance in mental maths. When awarding an end-of-year teacher assessment level, teachers also need to consider a child's performance on periodic and day-to-day assessments over all learning objectives.

Test 1: Mental maths assessment

Oral and mental questions (page 1 of 2)

Time: 20 minutes

- Read each question twice to the children.
- Answers to be recorded on the answer sheet on pages 108–110.
- One mark per question: 20 marks total.
- Allow five seconds for each answer for questions 1–5, ten seconds for questions 6–15 and fifteen seconds for questions 16–20.

	Question	Answer
1	What is 8 × 7?	56
2	Calculate 65 × 100.	6500
3	Fifty-four hundreds is the same as which number?	5400
4	How many do I add to $^3/_5$ to make one whole 1?	$^2/_5$
5	How many metres is 2460 centimetres?	24.6 metres
6	How many right angles are there in 360 degrees?	4
7	A regular hexagon has a perimeter of 42 centimetres. How long is each side?	7cm
8	Add 2.4 to 3.7.	6.1
9	*(Look at the numbers.)* I add a number to 325 to make 1000. Tick the correct number.	675
10	What is 5% of £3000?	£150

Test 1: Mental maths assessment

Oral and mental questions (page 2 of 2)

	Question	Answer
11	Write a prime number that is more than 50 but less 60.	53 or 59
12	25% of days in October will be windy. Tick the most appropriate statement.	uncertain
13	*(Look at the Venn diagram.)* Tick the number that is in the wrong position.	48
14	When I divide a number by 6 the answer is 40. What was my number?	240
15	*(Look at the fractions.)* Tick the fraction that is the same as ¼.	$^{3}/_{12}$
16	The area of a rectangle is 640 square centimetres. The length of one side is 20 centimetres. What is the breadth?	32cm
17	I am thinking of a number. I halve it and then add 20 to my total. My answer is 48. What was my number?	56
18	Six apples weigh 1.8 kilograms. How much would one apple weigh?	300g
19	Subtract two hundred from seven hundred and eighty-four.	584
20	I am facing south-west and turn clockwise through two right angles. What direction am I now facing?	north-east
End of test	**Total**	

Name Date

Test 1: Mental maths assessment

Oral and mental assessment answer sheet (1 of 3)

Time: 5 seconds per question

	Answer	Mark
1		
2		
3		
4		
5		

Time: 10 seconds per question

	Answer				Mark
6					
7					
8					
9	775	625	675	725	
10					

Name Date

Test 1: Mental maths assessment

Oral and mental assessment answer sheet (2 of 3)

Time: 10 seconds per question

	Answer				Mark
11					
12	fair ☐	uncertain ☐	certain ☐		
13	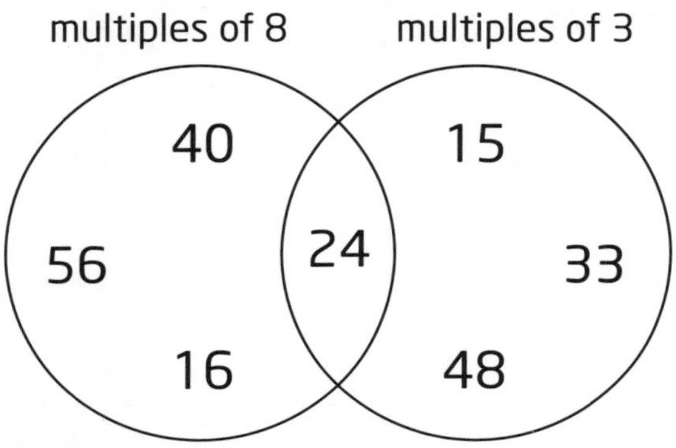				
14					
15	$\frac{3}{5}$	$\frac{3}{12}$	$\frac{5}{8}$	$\frac{2}{6}$	

1.2

Name Date

Test 1: Mental maths assessment

Oral and mental assessment answer sheet (3 of 3)

Time: 15 seconds per question

	Answer	Mark
16		
17		
18		
19		
20		
End of test	**Total**	

Mental maths teacher record sheet

Teacher's name: ______________________________

Name of starter	PNS objectives covered	Block/unit	Date activity was used

SCHOLASTIC

Also available in this series:

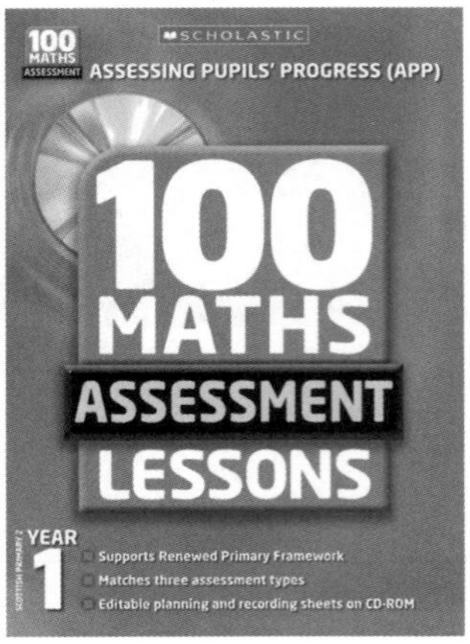

100 MATHS ASSESSMENT LESSONS Y1
ISBN 978-1407-10183-5

100 MATHS ASSESSMENT LESSONS Y2
ISBN 978-1407-10184-2

100 MATHS ASSESSMENT LESSONS Y3
ISBN 978-1407-10185-9

100 MATHS ASSESSMENT LESSONS Y4
ISBN 978-1407-10192-7

100 MATHS ASSESSMENT LESSONS Y5
ISBN 978-1407-10193-4

100 MATHS ASSESSMENT LESSONS Y6
ISBN 978-1407-10194-1

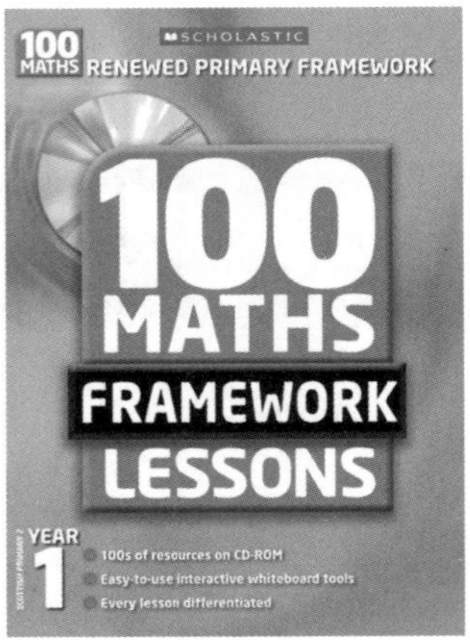

100 MATHS FRAMEWORK LESSONS Y1
ISBN 978-0439-94546-2

100 MATHS FRAMEWORK LESSONS Y2
ISBN 978-0439-94547-9

100 MATHS FRAMEWORK LESSONS Y3
ISBN 978-0439-94548-6

100 MATHS FRAMEWORK LESSONS Y4
ISBN 978-0439-94549-3

100 MATHS FRAMEWORK LESSONS Y5
ISBN 978-0439-94550-9

100 MATHS FRAMEWORK LESSONS Y6
ISBN 978-0439-94551-6

100 MATHS HOMEWORK ACTIVITIES Y1
ISBN 978-1407-10216-0

100 MATHS HOMEWORK ACTIVITIES Y2
ISBN 978-1407-10217-7

100 MATHS HOMEWORK ACTIVITIES Y3
ISBN 978-1407-10218-4

100 MATHS HOMEWORK ACTIVITIES Y4
ISBN 978-1407-10219-1

100 MATHS HOMEWORK ACTIVITIES Y5
ISBN 978-1407-10220-7

100 MATHS HOMEWORK ACTIVITIES Y6
ISBN 978-1407-10221-4

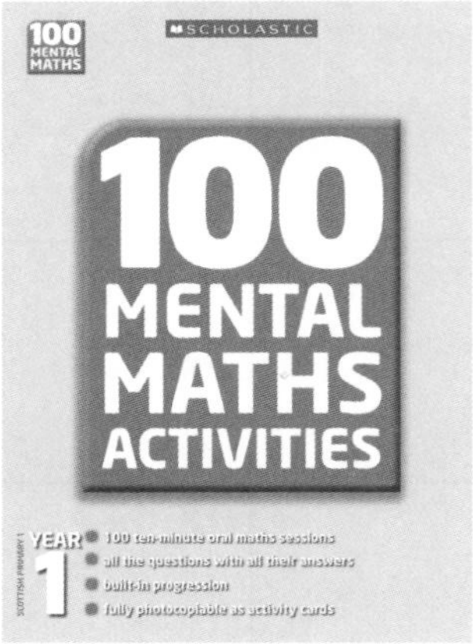

100 MENTAL MATHS ACTIVITIES Y1
ISBN 9781407114156

100 MENTAL MATHS ACTIVITIES Y2
ISBN 9781407114163

100 MENTAL MATHS ACTIVITIES Y3
ISBN 9781407114170

100 MENTAL MATHS ACTIVITIES Y4
ISBN 9781407114187

100 MENTAL MATHS ACTIVITIES Y5
ISBN 9781407114194

100 MENTAL MATHS ACTIVITIES Y6
ISBN 9781407114200

ONLINE

For further information, visit www.scholastic.co.uk/classpet